HYDRONIC

RADIANT HEATING

(A Practical Guide
for the Nonengineer Installer)

Dan Holohan

For additional copies, contact
HeatingHelp.com
63 North Oakdale Avenue,
Bethpage, NY 11714
Telephone: 1-800-853-8882
Fax: 1-888-486-9637
www.HeatingHelp.com

Manufactured in the USA

First Printing, April 1998
Second Printing, March 2000
Third Printing, February 2001
Fourth Printing, February 2002
Fifth Printing, November 2003
Sixth Printing, June 2005

ISBN 0-9743960-5-2

For Professor Mark Eatherton,
Colorado Madman, who knows an awful lot
about this subject
as well as another important matter,
that being the launching of small potatoes
into geosynchronous orbit.
Thanks, pal.

CONTENTS

. . . .

CHAPTER 1

. . . .

The Great Pickle Puzzle
(& other intimidations)

When I went to college, it was as a grown-up with four little daughters, a wife who had quit her job when the first kid arrived, and a monster mortgage that loomed dark and heavy over our heads. I went to college for no other reason than to get an education, and I studied the subject of sociology, which I have found to be the *perfect* major for any heating professional. Trust me on this. I graduated with a degree that would impress no one in the heating industry, but I learned lots of stuff about how we deal with each other.

Which brings me to the Great Pickle Puzzle.

I once visited a contractor in New York City. This guy did a lot of plan-and-spec work, which meant he had to deal with mechanical engineers just about every day of his working life. "Can't get away from them!" he said to me. "They make me crazy with some of the things they want me to do. I don't think they're allowed to go into boiler rooms or look at the equipment they specify. They just draw pictures of it all and hope I'm capable of doing the rest. They make me crazy."

At this point in our conversation, my eyes wandered to a shelf above his desk. There was a capped bottle sitting up there, the sort you get when you buy a Coke in a vending machine. Inside the bottle was the biggest damn pickle I had ever seen in my life. It nudged out to the sides and stretched from the bottom to the mouth of the bottle. What little space it left was filled with pickle juice. "What's with the pickle?" I asked.

"Oh, that?" he said, reaching up for it and handing it to me. "This is my Engineer Tester."

"How's it work?" I asked.

"It's simple," he said. "If you can tell me how I got the pickle in the bottle, you're *not* an engineer."

I stared at the bottle for a moment and then said, "You grew a cucumber inside the bottle, and then pickled it, right?"

"Right!" he said, snatching the bottle from my hands and placing it back on the shelf. "You can *never* be an engineer."

That incident stayed with me for a long time and one day I wrote a story about it in *Plumbing & Mechanical* magazine. I was curious to learn whether any engineers were reading this magazine, which was intended mainly for contractors. To find out, I told about the pickle, but I didn't give the answer. I wrote that if any engineer got frustrated, said engineer should go ask a contractor for the answer. Some fun, eh?

Turns out, *lots* of engineers read that magazine. *Lots* of them called me. They told me I was a stinking bum and that I should stop picking on engineers because they built the world and had all the answers. I was duly penitent.

One day, not long after, I received a call from a woman who said simply, "He can't sleep."

"*Who* can't sleep?" I asked.

"My husband," she said. "He read your article, and he hasn't been able to sleep for a week."

"He's an engineer, I take it?"

"Yes. I told him the guy in your story probably grew a cucumber in the bottle and then turned it into a pickle, but he said that was too simple. He figured the guy put a burning piece of paper into the bottle and then set the pickle on top of the opening. The oxygen burned up, creating a vacuum inside the bottle and the atmospheric pressure shoved the pickle down into the bottle. He knows that doesn't make much sense, but he's sticking with it because it's the best he can come up with at this point. The guy *did* grow the pickle in the bottle, didn't he?"

"Yes," I said.

"Thank you *so* much!"

"Can I ask you a question before you go?" I said.

"Sure."

"Did you go to college?"

"Uh huh," she said.

"What was your major?" I asked.

"Sociology," she said. "Why do you ask?"

"Just curious," I said.

And it didn't stop there!

Then I got a letter from a guy who *really* took me to task. He told me I was a stinking bum, and that I shouldn't be making fun of engineers. "We put men on the moon!" he wrote. When was the last time a heating contractor put a man on the moon?

He was upset.

He continued on in his letter to tell me he was qualified to heap criticism upon me because he was a licensed master plumber, and *also* a professional engineer. And *also* an *attorney.* Yikes!

The last sentence in his letter read, "And as for common sense, I want you to know that *I* know that the guy in your story grew the pickle in the jar!"

I wrote back and said, "Hmm, that would have worked, too, I suppose."

Never heard from the guy again.

Willard A. Gatzke, TL., DMT of Grand Junction, Colorado wrote me a note shortly after all of this began. I was pretty impressed with all those letters after his name, and his note explained what they meant. He told me that one time he was trying to tell an engineer that the design the guy proposed wouldn't work. "The engineer asked me for my business card," Willard explained. "At the time, my card just had my name, but no letters. The engineer looked at my card and then handed me *his* card. 'See those letters after my name?' he said. I looked and saw the letters PE, which, as you know, stand for Professional Engineer. I nodded my head indicating that I did indeed see those two letters. 'Well,' the engineer continued, 'as long as there are letters after *my* name and none after *yours*, what *I* say goes. Got it?'"

Willard told me the guy had upset him a bit, but had also given him a mighty fine idea. "I went out and had these cards made up," he said. "The ones that say, Willard A. Gatzke, TL., DMT."

"And what do the letters stand for?" I asked.

"Why, Dan, they stand for, These Letters Don't Mean a Thing. But when I show the card to an engineer, he or she does-n't know that, and he or she will *never* ask because engineers are supposed to know *everything*. I get more respect on those jobs nowadays.

How about that?

If you're a contractor, I suggest you have Ph.D. printed after your name on your business cards. It can stand for Plumbing, Heating, Drainage, or Professional Hydronics Designer. What do you think?

Couldn't hurt, right?

You *know* it!

Way back in 1992 when I wrote my first book, *The Lost Art of Steam Heating*, I opened with a quote from one of my favorite

Dead Men, Edward Richmond Pierce. While writing to the contractors at the turn of the last century, when central heating was brand new, Mr. Pierce said, "You know everything you need to know. You just don't know that you know it." What he meant was that most of what they needed to know about heating they had learned in grammar school. The same goes for you, pal. There's nothing to fear here; you just have to be confident. Most of this stuff just calls for common sense, and I *know* you have that.

Hydronic radiant heating obeys the basic laws of physics. You instinctively know these things: Heat goes to cold. High pressure goes to low pressure. Hot air rises; cold air falls. Air that doesn't have a difference in temperature hardly moves at all. You know these things. The trouble is, if you're not an engineer and the stuff you're reading is intended for engineers you're probably going to get confused by the special language they use. Engineering texts can confuse the heck out of you if you're not a member of the PE club. Here, for example, is a passage from Raber & Hutchinson's 1947 book, *Panel Heating and Cooling Analysis*. Hang onto your hat, Mr. Installer.

The equations for evaluating radiant-energy transfer in the heat-balance analysis of a panel heating or cooling system are modified forms of the basic rational equations for radiant exchange. Corresponding to a given value of the outside-air temperature, and for a room in which the panel area, total energy input and ventilation rate are fixed, the inside air and each point of every inside surface will reach equilibrium temperatures, which will be fixed with respect to time at values determined by the heat-transfer characteristics of the room.

Huh?

Raber and Hutchinson are tuned to a different station than the one I listen to. Did that gibberish hit you the same way it hit me? That stuff drives me crazy. I go into a paragraph and can't seem to find my way out. It puts me right to sleep, and I don't know about you, but I don't learn much when I'm sleeping. I like to keep things simple, and that's why whenever I get confused over something related to heating I always turn to my hero, Mr. Wizard. I grew up watching that guy on TV and I still catch him on Nickelodeon whenever I can. When my kids were smaller they had to compete in their grammar school's science fair and I always got them the Mr. Wizard books from the library for inspiration. I found a basic tenet of hydronic radiant heat in *Mr. Wizard's 400 Experiments in Science*. I think one of the reasons why God gives us children is so we can learn again what we may have forgotten from grammar school (you know everything you need to know; you just don't know that you know it.)

Anyway, here's what Mr. Wizard had to say (at least indirectly) about radiant heating.

Stand barefoot, with one foot on a rug and the other on tile (or wood). The tile feels cooler, even though it is at the same temperature, because it conducts heat away from your body more rapidly.

Ah yes! Rug feels *warm*! Tile feels *cool*! What could be simpler than that? And that, my friend, is the essence of hydronic radiant heating. As you shall see.

C H A P T E R   2

. . . .

Your Body is a Radiator!

Right now, as you sit reading this book, your body is producing about 500 BTUH. (That's British Thermal Units per Hour, in case you don't know. A BTU is the amount of heat it takes to raise the temperature of one pound of water one degree Fahrenheit.) You need only 100 BTUH to keep your brain thinking, your heart beating and your diaphragm moving in and out. The rest you have to shed. It's that shedding of heat that makes your body a radiator.

One of my old books, the *1934 American Society of Heating and Ventilating Engineers Guide* does a real good job of explaining this (even though an engineer wrote it).

The calculations for radiant heating are entirely different from those for convective heating. The purpose of convective heating is to determine the rate of heat loss from the room by conduction, convection, and radiation when maintained in the desired condition; radiant heating involves the regulation of the heat loss per square foot from the human body.

Get it? The point the guy was making is that hydronic radiant heating is *not* about the heat loss of the *room*; it's about the heat loss of the *person* in the room. Your body is a radiator! If you can control its heat loss, you will feel comfortable. It's as simple as that.

Here, listen to some of the key points the unnamed writer made in this book way back in 1934:

It has been pointed out that the human body loses heat to its environment in three ways: by convection, radiation, and evaporation. The Effective Temperature Chart takes account of convection and evaporation, but does not provide for such radiative effects as occur when room air and its surrounding surfaces differ widely in temperature.

What he's talking about here is a phenomenon called "Cold 70." It's the feeling you get when there's a big difference between the temperature of the air in a room and the temperature of the surfaces in that room. You've felt this before; I know you have. You ever go into a restaurant on a cold winter's day? The guy who greets you at the door seats you at a nice table near a plate glass window. What a view! You're sitting there for a just a few minutes, though, when your spouse complains that it's pretty cold at this table. You're feeling it too. Your right arm, which is the one closest to the window, is colder than your left arm. You ask the waiter if you can move to another table, and he puts you in the center of the dining room where you're both perfectly comfortable.

If you had a thermometer with you you'd find out something pretty surprising. The temperature of the air at the table near the window is exactly the same as the temperature of the air surrounding the table that's in the center of the dining room. The reason you felt so miserable when you were next to the window was because your body was losing too much heat to that cold surface. Your body is a radiator, and that uncomfortable feeling was "Cold 70."

I once gave a lecture at a resort in Ocean City, Maryland. This place was right on the beach and it had a big ice skating rink right in the lobby. You could sun yourself in the morning, and skate all afternoon. The Lovely Marianne and the daughters loved it.

That morning while I was getting ready for my lecture, one of the woman attendees showed up. She was wearing shorts and a tee shirt (it was a very casual seminar), and she was rubbing her arms furiously. "Where's the coffee?" she asked. "I'm freezing!"

"It's cold out there?" I asked.

"Oh yes!" she said. "I just walked here from my room and I had to go completely around that ice skating rink. It's really *cold* out there by that ice."

I knew I could use this in my seminar. After all, what is an ice skating rink but a hydronic radiant floor in reverse? As soon as the class began I asked them what temperature they thought it was in the room. They all guessed it was about 72 degrees F. I checked the air temperature with a digital thermometer I had brought along for the seminar. Sure enough, it was 72 degrees F. "How cold do you think it is out there by the ice?" I asked.

They looked at each other and laughed a bit. Then they decided it couldn't be more than 60 degrees F out there next to all that ice. "Let's go check it out," I said, and we headed out the door on a field trip.

When we got to the edge of the rink, I leaned over the railing and held the tip of my digital thermometer's probe about a foot off the surface of the ice. I let the number stabilize, and then I read it to the group. "It's 76 degrees F right here," I announced.

"It can't be!" the woman who had earlier complained about the cold said. "It's freezing right here!"

"See for yourself," I offered, showing her the thermometer.

"I don't care what that thing shows," she said. "It's how I *feel* that matters!"

Bingo!

She was feeling the full-blown effect of "Cold 70," and I was loving every minute of it! *This* is the core principle of hydronic radiant heating. It's how you *feel* that matters. You know that, right?

You know *everything* you need to know, pal.

Human heat loss

Your body loses heat by radiating it toward cooler objects, sure, but it also loses heat by convection and evaporation. Evaporation? That's sweating. You sweat, and the sweat evaporates, and you feel cool. Whenever a liquid turns to a vapor, heat goes with it. You know that, right? When you go outside during the winter you can see your breath, can't you? That's condensed moisture you're looking at. The same moisture leaves your body every moment of your life, and it always takes heat with it. But you only see it during the winter.

You also lose heat by convection when air passes over you. The faster the air moves, the more heat you lose. It's the same with a fan-coil unit. The faster the fan spins, the faster the heat leaves the coil, doesn't it? It's also the same with a convector in a cabinet. You can have a convector element that's six inches deep and 24 inches wide. If you put that element in a cabinet that's two feet high you'll get a certain output from it. But if you put that element in a cabinet that's *three* feet high you'll get even more output. Why? Because of the chimney effect. The velocity of the air increases so more of it moves across the element. The more air movement, the more heat loss.

When you fan yourself you feel cool even though the air temperature hasn't changed one bit. You feel cool because you're losing more heat. Get it? Your body's a fan-coil unit!

But let's get back to that book I was telling you about—the *1934 American Society of Heating and Ventilating Engineers Guide*. Listen to what the Dead Man has to say next.

When, however, the body is exposed to radiation from a hot surface or is radiating to a cold surface, the factor of radiative heat gain or heat loss may be important. This phenomenon is most marked in the case of exposure to the sun's radiative heat. On a cold day, with no wind blowing, while standing in the sunshine, one may feel perfectly comfortable, but when a cloud passes over the sun, one may instantly feel much cooler. The cloud acts as a shield to interrupt the radiant heat from the sun. The change in feeling of comfort is due to the instant change in the rate of heat loss from the body caused by the shielding effect of the cloud. A shielded thermometer under the same condition would register no change in temperature.

You've experienced that, haven't you? The sun goes behind a cloud and you feel cold. My daughters all play soccer, which means I stand in Soccer Hell on frigid Long Island days. Week after week I have to listen to the Soccer Mommies complain about how cold it gets every time a puffy cumulus cloud happens by. "It's so cold!" one will whine. "It was okay before, but as soon as the sun went behind the cloud I felt cold! Don't you feel cold?" My only protection from the Soccer Mommies is to launch into a discussion of radiant energy and its effect on the human body. I'll quote a few lines from the ol' Raber and Hutchinson book and they scurry away pretty quickly. That book has its uses after all!

When the sun ducked behind the clouds and the wind kicked up its heels, we felt even colder out there in Soccer Hell. And I *know* you know why.

The body's a radiator, right?

Consider, too, the *size* of the human radiator, and where you *put* it.

Again, from that 1934 ASHVE guidebook:

The rate of heat loss by convection depends upon the average temperature difference between the surface of the body and the surrounding air, the shape and size of the body and the rate of air motion over the body.

The guy on the Weather Channel calls this the Wind Chill Factor. You know all about that, don't you? Sure you do! It can be cold, but if it's cold *and* windy, you feel worse. Even though the air is the same temperature. You feel worse because that heat loss by convection combines with your heat loss by radiation and evaporation. This is getting *ridiculously* simple, isn't it? There's not that much to this hydronic radiant heating business. You don't need to be an engineer. You know everything you need to know.

And I'll bet you're even beginning to *know* that you know it. Again to the book:

The rate of heat loss by radiation depends upon the exposed surface area of the body, and upon the difference between the mean surface temperature of the body and the mean surface temperature of the surrounding walls or other objects. This latter temperature is called the Mean Radiant Temperature.

"Mean" is the position midway between the extremes. If the coldest temperature is 20 degrees F and the hottest is 90 degrees F, the mean temperature is 55 degrees F. That's all "mean" means. It *means* the same thing as "average." If you took the coldest temperature on your body (your toes) and the hottest temperature on your body (your choice!) the point in the middle of those two extremes would be your body's mean temperature. Do the same thing with the walls and the objects in the room and you'll come up with another number. The difference between those two numbers is the Mean Radiant Temperature of the room, which engineers also refer to as MRT. See? This should no longer be a scary term. There's nothing to this stuff! Why did that long-dead engineer/author use the word "mean" instead of the more understandable word "average" back in 1934? I figure he did it to confuse the average 1934 installer. That was *mean!*

At the temperature that produces comfort (and at all lower temperatures) the production of sweat is low and the heat loss by evaporation is relatively low and relatively constant, irrespective of the relative humidity of the atmosphere. Under such conditions the heat loss from the body is chiefly related to the combined effect of convection and radiation.

So you can see how important the temperature of the surfaces in a room, along with drafts, are to your comfort. Want to know why hydronic radiant heat feels better than furnace heat? With a scorched air system the air is always blowing around the room and over your body. That hot "draft" increases your body's heat loss by evaporation and convection. And since the temperature of the walls and objects in the room is relatively low (compared to what it is when you have a hydronic radiant system) you lose even more heat. So even though the air is scorched, you're uncomfortable.

But you got a good price, eh?

It's what's *outside* that counts (and how much of it there is!).

Under comfortable, still-air conditions during the heating season, the mean skin temperature of persons normally clothed is between 90 and 93 F (with lower values for the extremities), and the mean clothing temperature is between 82 and 86 F.

Go stick a thermometer on your shirtsleeve and you'll see what this guy was talking about in 1934. You're about 85 degrees F on the outside of your clothes. And that's why the goal in any hydronic radiant system is to make the floor a maximum of 85 degrees F on the coldest day of the year. If the floor is too hot, you'll feel uncomfortable because you'll retain too much heat.

Now, how about this?

It is necessary to determine the equivalent surface of the body from which heat is radiated and a similar value for convection. The total may be assumed to be about 19.5 square feet for convection and 15.5 square feet for radiation in an average sized individual.

Whoa! I don't know how they figured out the square footage of skin on people way back then in 1934. It sort of sets your imagination wandering, doesn't it? However they *did* it, they did it, and as you can see there's more of you subject to convective heat loss than there is to radiant heat loss. How come? Well, think about yourself for a moment. When the wind blows, it blows all over you, right? But when your body radiates, it radiates, in part, right back onto itself. The insides of your arms radiate onto your torso, and vice versa. The insides of your thighs radiant right at each other and one cancels the other. Think about what you do when it's really cold outside. You rub your arms with your hands, don't you? I'll bet you thought it was the friction that was making you feel warm. What you were really doing was quickly covering more parts of your body to lessen the radiant heat loss. Curl yourself up in a fetal position under those cold sheets on a cold winter night and you'll feel warmer, won't you?

And now you know why.

If you want to feel cooler on a hot summer day, try walking around with your legs stretched out as far as they will go, and your arms sticking straight up in the air. I *guarantee* people will give you more space when you walk around like this, and that's an added benefit!

On average, you'll lose about 80 BTUH through your nose, armpits, and whatever when you're just hanging around. That's your evaporative heat loss. Here's where the rest goes:

The balance of the heat generated in the average human body, approximately 300 to 320 BTUH at about 70 F room temperature, is the approximate amount of heat given off by radiation and by convection from the external body surfaces. Under normal conditions (in still air), the radiation loss will be about 190 BTUH and the convection loss about 120 BTUH.

How about that! You're losing nearly half of your body's heat production through radiation. That's what I mean when I say your body's a radiator. This is why the temperature of the stuff around you *really* matters. This is what makes hydronic radiant heating so very nice. When the stuff around you is the same temperature that you are, you feel *great*!

Heat *rises*. Or does it?

I checked back with Mr. Wizard and confirmed my suspicion that heat moves in one of three ways: conduction, convection, and radiation. Here's a somewhat official explanation of these three natural phenomena:

Conduction transfers heat through a substance because there's a difference in temperature between different parts of the substance. More-energetic (hotter) molecules transfer their motion to nearby, less-energetic (cooler) molecules, but a more effective method is the migration of energetic, free (and that doesn't mean "no charge") electrons. Metals are good conductors of both heat and electricity because they have a high density of free electrons.

There, that's official. You are very familiar with conduction. I know you learned it long ago on the day you touched that hot pipe. Remember?

A Mr. Wizard example of conduction would have you cooking a hot dog on a frying pan.

Hungry for more? Keep going.

Convection transfers heat by the flow of a liquid or gas. A fluid expands when you heat it, and when it does it decreases in density. In other words, it gets lighter. The warmer, less dense, part of the fluid will rise through the surrounding cooler fluid. If you continue to add heat, the cooler fluid that flows in to replace the warmer, rising fluid will also become heated and will rise, setting up a convection current.

Scorched air systems work by convection. They send the overheated air rocketing up toward the ceiling. The scorched air displaces the colder air, which falls to the ground (and all over you) in search of that elusive, typically undersized, return-air duct.

To describe convection, Mr. Wizard talks about cooking a hot dog over an open fire. The hot gases rise by convection and blast that doggie until it pops.

And that brings us to **radiation**, the most mysterious of the three. Radiation is the emission or transmission of energy in the form of waves through space. The rays from a radiator follow the same physical laws as the rays from the sun. The only difference is the rays from a radiator have a  longer wavelength than those that come to us from the sun. You can't see any of this, of course, so you'll just have to take my word for it.

Want to cook that hot dog by radiation? Stick it under a broiler.

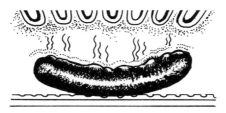

And that brings us to this business about heat rising. Heat doesn't actually "rise," you know. It moves through a solid object, or it rides on a gas or a liquid, or it flies through space. It goes toward cold because Mother Nature always wants to equalize everything. She hates imbalance. Hot *air* rises, not heat, but that's how this myth about "heat rising" got started.

Think about it. If heat rises, how come that hot dog got cooked? The broiler was higher than the hot dog, wasn't it? And how come you feel so warm when you switch on the heat lamp in that motel bathroom. Heat doesn't rise. *Hot air* rises. There's a difference, but you know that already, don't you?

You ever wonder about what goes on inside a microwave oven? The food gets hot, but the air inside the oven stays cool. You ever wonder about that? I think about stuff like that all the time. I'm forever asking questions like that. It drives The Lovely Marianne crazy.

Here, think about this. What goes on inside a microwave oven can help you better understand hydronic radiant heat. Microwaves can't "see" oxygen, hydrogen or nitrogen. Microwaves can, however, "see" carbon dioxide, water vapor, ozone, dust and any other airborne contaminants. The food gets hot, but the air, which is mostly nitrogen, oxygen and hydrogen, stays cool.

The radiant energy that comes off that warm hydronically heated floor works in a similar way, only with a different wavelength, which is very, very good for the people in the room. You don't want to be nuking the customers, do you?

Solar energy works in the same way as that warm floor and the microwave oven, but again, the wavelength is different. The solar energy that reaches the outer envelope of the atmosphere averages out at about 427 BTUH per square foot. Carbon dioxide, water vapor, ozone, dust and other airborne contaminants reduce this energy to about 275 BTUH per square foot by the time it hits the Earth's surface. Good thing for us! And this is why the ozone layer is so essential to human life, by the way. Ozone helps stop ultraviolet radiation, which can cause skin cancer.

Compare this 275 BTUH per square foot input load the sun provides to the 35 BTUH per square foot load (and that's the maximum!) we might put into a hydronic radiant floor. Big difference, eh? There's a lot of energy streaming down on us from outer space. When that energy gets into a house, you'll call it "solar gain." It can really screw up your calculations—both summer and winter—when you try to size a system. Sunlight goes in, but it doesn't go out.

Do you know why this is? When I travel to Europe I'm always fascinated by the way they put the shades on the outside instead of the inside of their windows (they use metal shades). They do this to keep the sunlight from getting through the glass because once it's inside the house, sunlight turns into something else.

You see, sunlight's shorter wave passes easily through glass without heating it significantly. But when the rays strike objects, they heat them and the objects then reflect radiant energy (which has a longer wavelength) into the room. These longer waves can't pass back through the glass so they get stuck inside the room and make it hotter and hotter.

And that's why it gets so brutally hot inside your car on a summer day. And that's why the Europeans put the shades on the *outside* of their windows instead of on the inside.

Further proof that heat doesn't rise

When Doris Duke was alive she was one of the richest women in the world, and one of her palatial homes was in central New Jersey. This place was bigger than a Home Depot. The Dead Men who built it heated it with hot water using a magnificent system of pipes up to ten inches in diameter. It was a thing of beauty, but it wasn't keeping her comfortable.

"There's hardly any heat on the first floor," the caretaker told me. "Upstairs is okay, but she's freezing down here. We'd like to hire you to figure out what's wrong."

"How long has this been going on?" I asked.

"Two years."

They built this place around 1890. It had a gravity hot water system with ten-inch mains, as I said. You ever see ten-inch mains? They're a lot bigger than ten inches! As I stared at them, I kept thinking about the strength of the Dead Men who hoisted all of this stuff into place. You ever see a ten-inch, screwed tee? It can make you sick to your stomach just looking at it.

Anyway, they heated the upper two floors with cast iron radiators and the first floor with indirect cast iron radiators, and that's where the trouble was. An old indirect radiator can be pretty intimidating. It looks like a meteorite-sized hunk of iron suspended inside a two-foot by three-foot duct. It could be a good-size boiler all by itself if it had a burner. That ductwork ran from the floor register in Doris Duke's living room (which was as big as a gymnasium) to a point in the basement wall where it abruptly ended just past the indirect radiator.

"It's too cold!" the in-house plumber said as I probed the floor register with a digital thermometer. The estate had an in-house plumber and an in-house just about every other trade you can think of. This woman didn't like to wait for service. "You have any idea what life is like when your entire world revolves around keeping one *very* powerful woman happy?"

"Yes, I do," I said, recalling that I have been wed to The Lovely Marianne for many years.

"Look at that air temperature," he said. "It's just 83 degrees F. It's *gotta* be hotter than that when it leaves the register."

"Let's take a look in the basement," I said.

"Might as well," he sighed. "The trouble's here, but I guess we should look around."

When I opened the duct's access door to the indirect heater, it felt like I'd just popped open a brick oven.

"Whew!" the plumber said, "There's plenty of heat in *there*. And that's what's confusing the heck out of me. It just won't go *upstairs*. It should because there's nothing in its way, and heat rises, right?" He pointed to the old iron radiator. It was just a few feet away from the floor register. We could see light shining down. "It looks like we're defying a basic law of physics here, Dan," he said. "Heat *does* rise, you know."

He knew everything he needed to know. He was just confused.

"Do you have the damper open to the outside air?" I asked, pointing at the place where the ductwork ended abruptly at the basement wall. "This goes outside, you know."

"Yeah, it's wide open," he said. "Has been for two years. I even put a fan inside that one over there." He took me over and showed it to me. It was a small electric fan that was shaking its little head back and forth in a sad way, and to no avail. "I figured I could *push* the heat through faster with the fan, but no dice, it just hovers around the radiator and won't move upstairs. I don't get it. Heat *rises*."

"Let's put our heads together here for a minute," I said. "If *you* were heat, why wouldn't *you* rise?" I asked him.

"Huh?" he said.

"If you were heat, why wouldn't you rise?" I repeated, "And is it really *heat* that's rising?"

"What do you mean?"

"Well, isn't it the *air* that's supposed to rise? Not the *heat*. The *air*."

"If you want to be picky about it, I suppose so," he said.

"I want to be picky about it," I said. "If *you* were air, why wouldn't *you* rise?"

"The only thing I can think of," he said, "would be if there was nothing to take my place."

"Right! Air has weight and it takes up space. For it to rise, *something* has to take its place, right?"

"I guess. More air, right?"

"Yeah, more air," I said. "And that's where the mystery lies because that outside air damper is wide open."

"Then how come the air isn't moving?" he said.

"Are you *sure* the dampers are wide open?" I asked.

"Absolutely."

"But what's on the other side of the damper?" I asked.

"I don't know. I never looked."

"We really should," I said.

We walked around the outside of the mansion to the place where we thought the duct should come out, but we saw nothing but shrubs and ivy.

"Where does that duct come out?" I asked.

"Beat's me," he said. "I've never looked for it out here. It's gotta be around here someplace."

We stomped around in the dirt for a few minutes until we heard a hollow "Thump!" We started kicking dirt out of the way. Something flat and white showed through. We kept kicking dirt. Then we got smart and grabbed a shovel.

It turns out there was a 4' X 8' piece of fiberglass and six inches of mulch covering the fresh air inlet to the duct. When the caretaker lifted it, the smoke from his cigarette shot straight down into the hole.

"I'll be darned," he said.

We felt the difference in temperature as soon as we walked back into that great big living room. Heat was pounding out of the floor register. Back outside, we found four more intake ducts covered in the same way.

"Can't blame the butler," I said.

"Nope, the gardener did it!" he said.

"Heat doesn't rise," I said.

"I will remember that all the days of my life," he said. And so should you.

Heat doesn't fall either

As I write these words it is seven AM on a beautiful summer morning. I'm sitting on a couch in a hotel room in Portland, Oregon and I just took a shower. There was a heat lamp in the bathroom that glared to life when I switched on the exhaust fan. I instantly felt its warmth. In fact, it was a bit warmer than I wanted it to be on a nice summer morning, but I didn't have much of a choice. The thing was wired in series with the exhaust fan. Breath or roast—those seemed to be my options. I found a third option, though. I reached up and unscrewed the bulb.

And this got me thinking again about hydronic radiant heat because I am a Wet Head. Heat doesn't rise, and it doesn't fall. It moves from a hot place to a cold place in one of three ways – by conduction, convection or radiation. In this case, I was feeling the radiation.

I remember, too, how I once left my rental car with a valet parking attendant one winter's evening in Chicago. When I came out of the restaurant a few hours later I stood under an infrared heater while I waited for the guy to retrieve the car. I felt warm, even though it was only about 25 degrees F that night. I felt warm because heat doesn't rise. On that cold night, it radiated right down on me, and I thought of the nature of an infrared heater.

Heat doesn't rise. But you know that, don't you?

A Canadian who said it *very* well

In 1990, about the time when hydronic radiant heating was just being reborn in America, a Canadian engineer, L. H. LaFontaine, wrote an article for *Heating/Piping/Air Conditioning* magazine. Oh, how I wish more engineers would learn to speak this way. Listen:

Nothing is as misunderstood as the obvious. At the beach on a bright, sunny day, the sand feels hot underfoot, the ocean water by comparison seems icy cold, and the asphalt pavement is scorching. After sundown, the sand is already cool, the ocean remains at the same temperature it was during the day, and the asphalt is still very warm.

Why does the earth warm up and cool down faster than a large body of water? Why does sand lose its heat faster than asphalt? It's all a matter of the selectivity of the surface. Water has a reflective surface and heats up slowly as it reradiates solar electromagnetic waves to the atmosphere; it keeps its heat longer for the same reason. Sand is of light color and its texture is porous while asphalt is dark and quite dense. The asphalt is a good heat sink while the sand is not.

In the desert, temperatures may rise above 100 degrees F during the day yet drop to below freezing at night. In essence, it is not the ambient air temperature that we feel but the radiant rays or reflected rays. This would lead us to believe that the air temperature is not really what is read by the thermometer. The air temperature is much lower, and it is falsified by the radiant rays. Another example is sunbathing in early spring, when some people use the snow's reflective rays to enhance the tanning process. But they scurry for their parkas whenever a cloud passes by. The ambient air temperature does not drop that quickly. We believe the air temperature would be even lower than the one measured in the shade of the cloud since the temperature would still be affected by irradiation from various sources such as nearby buildings, sunlit snow-covered hills, etc.

How're you doing? You've been to those places, haven't you? The beach. That hot parking lot. That snowy field on a sunny day. You know everything you need to know. You know it *instinctively*, and this fellow does a fine job of explaining it, doesn't he? Oh, how I wish more engineers would speak that way.

Remember, your body is a radiator

Need more everyday examples? Okay, how's this? In your neighborhood supermarket, you will find everything you need to explain hydronic radiant heat to a layperson. In these magnificent laboratories you will find the cereal aisle, the frozen-food aisle, the deli counter and the housewares aisle. Stop first in the housewares aisle and pick up a cheap, mercury thermometer. You'll find them hanging from a hook. Lay that thermometer in your shopping cart and walk over to the cereal aisle. Check out the temperature. Got it? Good! Now stroll over to frozen foods. Notice how chilly you feel when you round the corner and get close to those cold freezers. Now check out the thermometer. Notice how it hasn't changed by a single degree? That's that phenomenon I told you about before. We called it "Cold 70." Remember that? The air temperature and the temperature of the surrounding surfaces are wildly different in that frozen-food aisle and you're feeling it.

Okay, now take a walk over to the deli counter. You see that chicken rotisserie? Sure smells good, doesn't it? Get a little closer. Notice how warm you're feeling? That's because the rotisserie is hotter than you are. It's radiating at you, sure, but it's also not letting your body lose that heat, and that's why you feel so uncomfortably warm. This is also why you have to design your radiant systems well because if you make the floor hotter than 85 degrees F, your customers will feel too warm and they'll complain.

Pay attention to the world around you; there's science everywhere, and that science can help you sell this stuff.

Consider a simple sliding glass door, for instance. I once helped out a guy who had a hydronic radiant heating system. He was bald and he was miserable. Not because he was bald, mind you, but because whenever he leaned back in his recliner he felt uncomfortably cold. He was okay when he was sitting straight up, but as soon as he leaned back, he felt cold.

I'm sure you can figure out why. That bald head pointed at that cold sliding glass door and fired off BTUs like a machine gun fires bullets. He was losing most of his body heat through the top of his noggin. The solution? We moved the chair.

Simple solutions are *good* solutions, aren't they?

I sat at a football game at the University of Notre Dame (Go Irish!) one day and felt warm because I was sitting on one of those butt-warmers that sporting goods stores sell to hunters. It was bright orange and very cozy. It was filled with little Styrofoam pellets and that's what kept my big butt from losing its heat. I thought of this as I watched the Fighting Irish do battle because I am a Wet Head, and Wet Heads are always thinking about science and heating. It's everywhere! Pay attention and you'll find all sorts of things you can use to sell hydronic radiant heat.

In 1990 I was foolish enough to take on the New York City Marathon. When I finished the 26.2-mile course and crossed the finish line, still alive and quite pleased with myself, a volunteer ran up and covered me with this "blanket" made from Mylar. It was cold in Central Park on that mid-November day, but I felt warm instantly when that young woman covered me. You know why? Because Mylar is shiny and it reflected my radiant heat back onto my poor aching body. It also kept the wind off of me so I lost less heat through convection. I had just run the Marathon, but I was thinking about heating. This is because I am a Wet Head.

There's no question about it; your body's a radiator, pal. Get used to it.

CHAPTER 3

. . . .

Convection or Radiation?

So now we come to the question of what's the best way to heat a room. You really have just two choices. You can do it by convection, or by radiation. One of the old books in my collection, *Audels Plumbers and Pipe Fitters Library*, shows these options. First, they show you a room they've heated with a cast iron, hot water radiator.

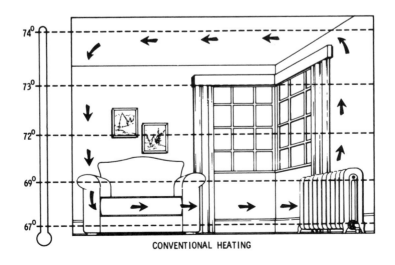

CONVENTIONAL HEATING

The temperature just above the floor is 67 F, right? But notice how the temperature at the ceiling is 74 F. The temperature five feet above the floor is 72 F. The difference in temperature proves that hot air rises and cold air falls. There are convective currents of air moving like a Ferris wheel in this room.

In the same book on another page there's a drawing of a room heated by a hydronic radiant system installed in the ceiling. Here it is.

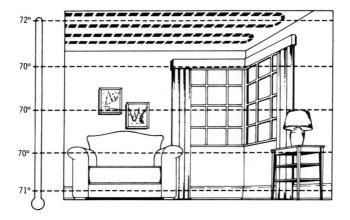

As you can see, the temperature just above the floor is 71 F. The temperature at the ceiling is 72 F. The temperature five feet above the floor is 70 F.

You see the difference? The radiant system doesn't allow the air to move much by convection. It's working by casting radiant energy down upon the people and the objects in the room. There are a couple of disadvantages to ceiling hydronic radiant heat, though. It can increase the heat loss in a one-story building because it makes the ceiling so warm, and you'll feel greater warmth around your head and shoulders than you will around your feet. It's nice, but it's not as nice as hydronic radiant heat in the floor. It's also not practical in buildings with very high or very low ceilings. The radiant effect, like light, varies in inverse proportion to the distance. In other words, the closer you get to it, the hotter it feels. Vice versa too.

I have this other book in my collection, and it's a classic. T. Napier Adlam wrote it in 1934 and called it, simply, *Radiant Heating*. There's a drawing in this book that shows a room heated with a cast iron steam radiator.

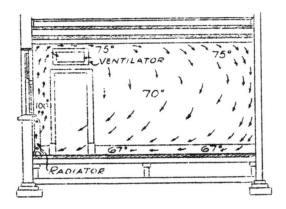

The temperature just above the floor is 67 F. The temperature at the ceiling is 75 F. The temperature directly above the steam radiator is 100 F. Yikes! The temperature five feet above the floor is 70 F. Lots of convection going on in this room, eh?

Next, he has a drawing that shows a room heated with a hydronic radiant system installed in the floor.

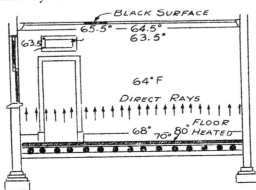

The temperature just above the floor is 68 F. The temperature at the ceiling is 65.5 F. The temperature five feet above the floor is 64 F. The temperature of the floor's surface is 80 degrees F.

Finally, he shows a drawing of a room heated with a scorched-air furnace.

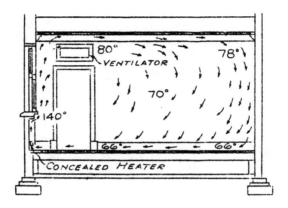

The temperature just above the floor is 66 F. The temperature at the ceiling is 80 F. The temperature directly above the scorched-air register is 140 F–ouch! The temperature five feet above the floor is 70 F.

Pretty screwy, eh? It's tough to get comfortable in this room. Notice, too, the difference between radiant and scorched air when it comes to the air temperature at the ceiling. Scorched air, by the way, is why we put so much insulation in ceilings. When the air is that hot, there's just naturally more heat loss to the cold attic. If you can lower the temperature of the air at the ceiling, you will lower the fuel bills. And that's exactly what hydronic radiant heat does.

You know that instinctively, don't you? You know that heat loss varies with the difference in temperature between what's inside the room and what's outside the room. Here, the difference between scorched air and radiant is 14.5 F! That makes a huge difference. And with less convective movement of air (as you'll have with radiant) there will also be less infiltration through the windows and doors. That means there will be less dust in the room as well. Also, since furnaces very often have oversized fans that pressurize the room, forcing the scorched air out through every crack in the walls, you get more heat loss through exfiltration.

Hydronic radiant heat gets all of that nonsense out of your life. It saves you money while making you more comfortable. And it does the same for your customers. All you have to do is tell them about it!

T. Napier Adlam worked for Sarco, the same folks who are so prominent in steam heat nowadays. Back in the Thirties and Forties, Sarco was just as big in hydronic radiant heating, and Mr. Adlam was their resident guru. Listen to what he had to say about the Liverpool Cathedral in England:

When the temperature of the air at four feet above the floor was 60 degrees F, it was found that the air temperature at the tirforium level, more than 90 feet above, was $58^1/_2$ degrees F, just $1^1/_2$ degrees F lower than at four feet above the floor. It seems to me that no other known method of heating could create these ideal conditions in such a high building, because I have conducted tests in similar cathedrals where warm air systems have been installed and the temperature at that high level is much too hot to be comfortable.

See what I mean about convective currents of air? Here he had this ceiling that soared 90 feet into the air, and yet the air temperature varied by less than two degrees F. Imagine how nice this feels in a regular house. And think about how well suited hydronic radiant heating is for a fancy house with a cathedral ceiling. This is the sort of thing you should tell your customers about. It's in their self-interest, right?

Off the wall

You can also install a hydronic radiant system in a wall, but this can set up convective currents because the air on the heated side of the room will rise, and the cooler air on the other side of the room will fall. You avoid that when you put the tubing in the floor or the ceiling because the warm surface extends across the whole room. There's no place for the cooler air to fall toward.

I'll give you a good analogy of this—at least *I* think it's a good analogy! Back in the days when the Dead Men installed gravity hot water heating systems they would connect freestanding, cast iron radiators with the inlet and the outlet at the bottom of the radiator. They did this because they didn't use circulators. The hot water would enter the radiator and drift upward into the cast iron sections, displacing the cooler water that was already in the radiator. This cooler water would fall out of the radiator through that pipe on the opposite end.

When you add a circulator to this system, the hot water zips right through the radiator's lower push nipples – in one end and out the other. This slows the convective movement of the water within the radiator because the colder water can't fall *out* of the radiator. There's hot water all the way across the bottom! You wind up with a radiator that's hot at the bottom and cold at the top. The trick to solving this one is to slow the flow into the radiator by throttling the inlet valve. You want more heat so you *close* the valve. It doesn't make sense, but it works.

In a room that has hydronic radiant heat in the floor, the air doesn't move much because the entire floor is warm. Just like the entire bottom of that old, cast iron radiator was warm. Does that analogy work for you? I sure hope so.

Nowadays, engineers in Europe are designing hydronic radiant heat into the lower part of walls that have large windows. The warmth that flows off the lower part of the wall counteracts the cooler air that's trying to fall from the cold surface of the window. Their goal is to stop the convective movement of air and it works very well. It also gets them around the challenge of nails. People are *much* less likely to hang a picture on the lower part of a wall, right?

Heat to spare!

T. Napier Adlam went on in his book to say something else about the Liverpool Cathedral that I already suspected from living in my neighborhood here on Long Island, but nevertheless I found this fascinating. Here, listen.

Another remarkable feature is the thermal storage of the structure, for it is found that if the oil furnaces are turned off, it takes 36 hours for the temperature in the cathedral to fall one degree F. It has been found in actual operation throughout the winter, that if the fires are operated for a few hours only each day, the temperature change is so small it cannot be detected on the thermometer, regardless of any change in the outside temperature.

Once you heat a slab of concrete, it holds heat for a long, long time. That's why they could shut off the burners and still have a warm floor a day and half later. I've seen this happen many times right in my hometown. I grew up on Long Island where many of the homes have hydronic radiant heat. They built these homes after World War II because it was one of the least expensive ways to build tract housing. They just laid copper tubing on the ground and poured concrete over it. Even when the systems were this crude, they still lasted for decades.

Most of our electrical wires hang from poles overhead, and whenever we have a big snowstorm, lots of trees come crashing down on these wires. We can lose our electricity for days. If this happens during the winter, we're in big trouble, unless we live in one of those wonderful old homes with the warm slabs. Then we can be without power for three or four days and our homes will *still* be warm. There's a *lot* of energy stored in a rock that size!

Mr. Adlam was working at a time when controls were primitive. About the best thing around was the Sarcotherm control, which his company manufactured. Here's what it looked like.

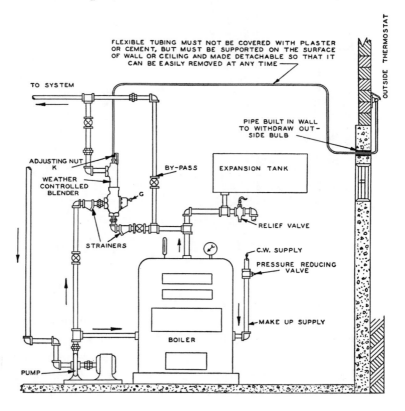

The Sarcotherm sensed outdoor air temperature with a temperature-sensitive bulb that stuck out through a wall on the north side of the building. It was a non-electric valve and it mixed the hot boiler water with some of the water that flowed back from the radiant panel. It was one of the first outdoor "reset" systems.

Dead Men used a similar control strategy when they built those homes on Long Island after World War II. This "control" didn't respond to changes in outdoor temperature, though. It was just a simple $^3/_4$" x $^1/_8$" bushing they would install near a bypass line to divert most of the water returning from the radiant panel back out to the panel.

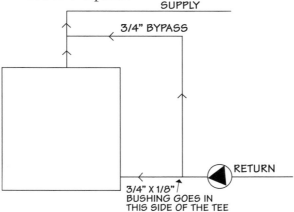

Only the return water that would fit through that $^1/_8$" hole in the bushing went back to the boiler. And when it did, the same amount of hot water left the boiler to heat the bypassed flow of water. It was crude, but it worked fairly well. These homes had a boiler that served just one heating zone. Each boiler also had a tankless coil for domestic hot water. The Dead Men maintained 180-degree boiler water (for the tankless coil), and mixed just enough hot supply water into the bypassed water to give them 140-degree water for the radiant system.

All of these jobs burned fuel oil and when the tankless coil fouled after a number of years, the oil company's service technician would boost the boiler temperature. This made the floors a lot hotter than they were supposed to be. The asbestos flooring tiles, which were standard in these homes, became mushy as the temperature increased. The legs of the furniture and women's high heels often dug holes in the tiles. When the floor got *really* hot, the tiles came loose and skidded around the room like hockey pucks.

Nowadays, the controls you can get for your hydronic radiant systems are much more accurate and, since they're electronic, they're about as simple as that old $^3/_4$" x $^1/_8$" bushing to install. They keep the slab from getting too hot, and they maintain a level of comfort that's unsurpassed by any other type of central heating system, but more on this later. For now, I just want to get you acquainted with some basic concepts, and to let you know that you won't be the first to install one of these systems. Here, let me share a letter with you that a fellow in Washington State shared with me not too long ago.

North to Alaska

Dear Russ:

It has now been a little over a year since I first contacted you concerning radiant heating. At that time, this form of heating was strictly a novelty with us, and we had a few mental reservations as to how well it would work up here in the "frozen North."

However, we are well past our winter up here, and to say that our heating plant has proven out well is certainly an understatement. We are well pleased with its performance. During the winter, with its sudden changes in temperature and its winds, the temperature in our store remained unvarying at the temperature desired. Our oil consumption was approximately 1,000 gallons per month. We expect to better this figure considerably next winter, as we will improve our insulation of the building.

Our plant has performed with no trouble whatever. The heat is steady, with no noise and no circulation of dust and dirt. It is fully automatic, requiring only an occasional check.

I am sorry that we have no pictures available of the new building right now, but possibly I will remember to send you one when we get some made. Our only regret is that we did not install radiant heating under the sidewalk in front of the building. We really had a lot of snow this winter.

Sincerely,
G.H. Gilson, Manager
Gilson Mercantile Co.
Valdez, Alaska

R.E. "Russ" Storwick of Renton, Washington mailed me a copy of that letter. "I share this with you," he said, "because I want to impress upon the trade that they have not discovered anything new with hydronic radiant heat." The date on the Gilson letter, by the way, is April 16, 1949, nine months before I was born.

Along those lines, R.E. Storwick, whom I know only through the mail, mentions the following in his letter to me. "You may have wondered why I have not signed up for any of your meetings in this area. The reason is that I have been in this field for over fifty years, and made about every mistake that is possible, and never the same mistake twice. This, plus the fact that if I tried to make all of the money in the country, the government would find a way to take it back."

I *like* this guy.

Listen to how R.E. Storwick of Renton, Washington got to meet G.H.Gilson of Valdez, Alaska. "This gentleman just happened to hear about the systems that we were designing and then he looked us up at our shop. The end result was that he gave the dimensions of the building he wanted to heat. I knew the country as I had been to Valdez a couple of times in the Thirties when I was in the Merchant Marine."

See? A great reputation can easily leap across state lines. If you're competent in hydronics, people will find you—especially if you're competent in *radiant* hydronics.

"I have read that they used this form of heating eons ago in

Korea," R.E. Storwick continues. "The only thing different was that they used hollow tile for the floor to let the flue gases find their way out. How they controlled the system is another thing. Even the controls on *our* systems leave something to be desired, though."

I like a person with strong opinions and a sense of history, don't you?

As he was acquiring those 50 years of experience, he was also learning things about pipe. Listen.

"I have advocated the use of steel pipe only; there are several reasons for this, and they are basically very fundamental. In the first place, steel pipe bonds to the concrete floor or the plaster ceiling. Secondly, the heat that transfers out of the steel pipe parallels with concrete or plaster, therefore giving a faster response. I did use copper tubing at first, but then I found that the heat transfer through the copper was too fast. Then the copper would harden and it would break and leak.

"I did see an advertisement about 'Bundy' tubing, and I figured this was the answer. I was not in a position to try it as I was working for a professional engineer at the time and I knew that he would not try something that was not accepted. After I got my own business, I tried to locate the company, but to no avail. They must have given up the ghost and left the scene.

"In my home, I have the coils in the floor in the lower living area, with the pipes on twelve-inch centers. In my garage, they are on twenty-four-inch centers. The water temperature runs at about ninety degrees Fahrenheit, modulated through a Taco 'Paneltrol.' [This device was similar to the Sarco control of the same era. D.H.] Even with that, it gets more than comfortable in about thirty minutes. In the ceiling of the main living area, the center-to-center spacing varies from twelve inches in the living room, dining room and kitchen to about eighteen inches in the bedrooms and the baths. This is controlled in the same way. But being in the plaster ceiling, there is no direct sense of feeling the heat. The wall-to-wall rugs, being of a pastel color, absorb the radiation from the ceiling, making the room comfortable with ninety-degree water."

Hydronic radiant heat has been around for a long time. You won't be the first, pal. Don't worry.

And R. E. Storwick wasn't the first either!

Not by a long shot! You have to go back to the Romans to find the first radiant heating systems. They used them to heat their baths between about 80 BC and 450 AD. For 530 years, and starting at a time before Jesus was born, they proved that radiant heat works. You *won't* be the first.

The Romans had a system called a hypocaust. Here's a drawing of one.

They built a fire in a hole just outside the building and vented the hot gases under the building. The gases warmed the stone and the water on the way out. Years later, Europeans heated their castles the same way. Check it out.

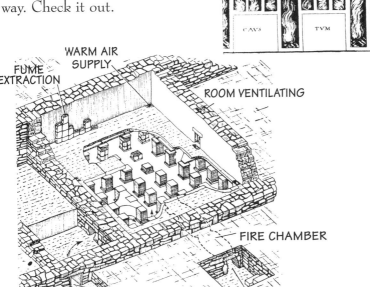

After the castles, radiant heat took a break for a thousand years or so. People were too busy romping around the countryside and killing their neighbors to worry much about heating buildings. We see the science reemerge in 1929 in Holland where some smart engineer designed it into an Amsterdam school. The following year, another smart engineer put one into a bank in England. He chose to put this one into the ceiling. Here it is.

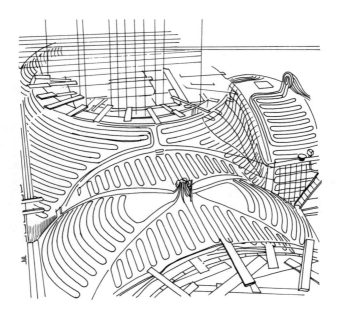

The first modern American system went into the British Embassy in Washington DC, and this also happened in 1930— you *won't* be the first! I had a guy in my seminar in 1995 who had recently worked on that system's boiler. "It's still going strong, Dan," he reported. I was glad to hear it; a well-designed hydronic radiant heating system can stick around for a long, long time. All of these early systems wound up in plaster ceilings. They did it this way because they could let the surface temperature of the ceiling exceed 85 degrees F. No one walks on a ceiling, you see.

They didn't worry about the plaster's effect on the pipes, because they used mostly wrought iron in those days. They allowed for a gap around the edge of the ceiling, which gave the ceiling room to expand. They hid the gap with molding. They did a good job, and that's why these systems are still working today.

In 1946, following World War II, a pamphlet titled, *Domestic Heating in America—A Study of Heating, Cooking, and Hot Water Supply in Small Homes in the USA and Canada*, appeared. In it, the author made this observation:

> *Britain is regarded as the home of radiant panel heating; however, considerable developments are taking place in America. This suggests we should follow up on our pioneer efforts by further experimental development of the system for application to small houses. The accepted surface temperatures for floors are considerably higher in America than in Britain, which suggests there is an area worthy of investigation.*

The British had been concerned about putting metal pipes in concrete because they thought bad things would happen to the metal. But in America, builders of tract housing were doing it every day, and those systems seemed to work. The British finally got over their fears when they made studies of buildings that had been bombed during the war. They found that pipes embedded in reinforced concrete were in better shape than those that been exposed to outside air. This gave them encouragement, and it changed the way they installed their systems.

Here in America, the Chase Brass & Copper Company built a test house that represented the most difficult house to heat that I can imagine when it comes to radiant.

This place had three exposed walls, a cathedral ceiling, a crawl space, and skylights. These are all things you need to watch out for when you're sizing a hydronic radiant system, as you will see. Chase used a ceiling-mounted system, and supplemented it with rows of copper tubing between the joist bays. This was the first of what we today call a "staple-up" system. They published their findings in 1945 in a classic book called the *Chase Radiant Heating Manual* and it changed a lot of things in America.

CHAPTER 4

· · · · · · · ·

A Place Called Levittown

The work Chase Brass & Copper did inspired a man named William Levitt in 1947. He was the first guy to build homes by following the example of mass production invented by Henry Ford. Levitt called his creation, "Levittown," and it remains a vibrant community today. I know it well because it is the town next door to Bethpage, which is where I live.

In a book about Levittown, Long Island historian Bernice Marshall had this to say:

For the first time, mass production methods were employed in erecting these 10,000 homes. There were workers whose jobs consisted of painting front stoops. Others did nothing more than install doorknobs. To such an extent was specialization carried.

William Levitt wanted his town to be the perfect place for young families. He marketed his homes to GIs who were returning from World War II. You didn't need to put down much money to own a Levitt house, and they sold quickly.

Levitt didn't want the expense of having to excavate basements. At the time, there was a law in the town of Hempstead, where Levittown was to be, that prohibited the construction of homes without basements. Hempstead, along with the rest of Long Island, was then and remains today a Republican stronghold. New York City, on the other hand, was heavily Democratic. William Levitt wanted to build homes without basements so he could keep the costs as low as possible. He chose to heat them with hydronic radiant heat because that was the least expensive system he could find. The trouble was the politicians in Hempstead Town feared that if Levitt built these low-cost homes, Democrats from New York City would move out in droves and change the power structure of the place.

William Levitt lobbied the Federal government when he wasn't able to get anywhere with the local politicians. He explained that he wanted to build these homes for the heroes returning from the war. His argument won out, and he built his town. Sure enough, the Democrats moved out from New York City and bought homes. But as it turned out, the politicians had nothing to fear because as soon as those New York City Democrats became Long Island homeowners, most of them also became Republicans.

William Levitt's houses went up so quickly (one every two hours!) that there really wasn't that much time to spend with any individual heating system. He built them well enough, but not perfectly. He didn't, for instance, use a vapor barrier under the concrete slabs. You need a vapor barrier to keep the moisture in the ground from stealing heat from the slab. The barrier also lets you know if there's a leak in one of your pipes. Without the barrier, a leaking pipe will just drain into the ground and you'll never know it's happening until you get the biggest fuel bill of your life.

Mr. Levitt also didn't bother with edge insulation around his concrete slabs. Without the insulation, the heat from the slab migrates out into the ground surrounding the home. He didn't use any insulation under the slab either. This is why you can now drive through Levittown on a cold day in late February and see tulips growing. The homeowners are very proud of their extended growing season; they think it's because they have green thumbs. I think it's because the ground outside their homes is nearly as warm as the concrete slabs under their homes. You *need* that edge insulation.

His mass-production techniques kept the costs down, but they also led to some trouble with the copper tubing as time went by. I once met a guy who worked on those Levitt homes. He told me they used steel horseshoe nails to attach the copper tubing to the wood frames. "To keep it from shifting when we poured the concrete," he said.

Those metals are dissimilar and that led to corrosion and leakage in some Levitt homes. Pipes would sometimes snap as slabs settled and cracked. They didn't cut control joints in these slabs; speed was the thing in those days. Get 'em built!

All of this, of course, led to leaks under the slab, but few homeowners knew what was happening because there were no vapor barriers under those slabs. The water went down, not up. They'd get these high fuel and water bills, which they often thought were normal because this didn't happen overnight.

When things got really bad and the boiler was taking on so much feed water that the people living in the home couldn't take a decent shower, they'd usually call their oil company and ask for help. Most of the homes on Long Island have oil heat. The service technician would show up and suspect the worst. Then he'd have to figure out where the leak was. He'd get down on his hands and knees and crawl around the floor, trying to hear the water running within the concrete slab. When he thought he heard something, the tech would listen with the back end of a screwdriver held to his ear. He would touch the screwdriver's point to the spot where he suspected the leak to be. As years went by and the trouble persisted, these guys began to use stethoscopes, which they found to be easier on their ears.

One old-timer told me a story about a woman who once helped him find a leak. "And she wasn't even in the business!" he said. She watched him crawl around on the kitchen floor, listening with the butt end of his screwdriver. "What are you doing?" she asked.

"I'm trying to listen for the leak," he said from under the kitchen table.

"What does it sound like?" she asked.

"Oh, just like water running. It's not so loud, and that's why everything has to be quiet," he said, hoping she would take the hint, but it was no use.

"Can I help?" she asked.

"No, it's all right."

"You sure there's nothing I can do to help?"

"It's all right."

"You're sure?"

"I'm *sure*," he said, trying to hear the water over her nonstop yakking.

"Why is it so bad when the water leaks?" she asked. "Is that why I can't get the shower water hot? What does the shower have to do with the floor? The shower's in the bathroom, and you're looking in the kitchen."

Totally frustrated, he leaned back on his haunches and did his best to explain what was going on in a way she would understand, hoping she would then just shut up. "Look," he said. "The water travels through the buried pipe, just like a car going down the road." He gestured with hands, like a car going down the road. "If the pipe breaks, the water won't go down the road; it will go into the ground. If the water's in the ground, it can't carry the heat to where you need the heat to be. That's what I'm trying to listen to. I want to find where the heat isn't going straight." He gestured again, like a long, straight road.

"If the heat doesn't go straight, which way will it go?" she asked.

"Well, first it goes sideways in a big splotch, and then it just goes away," he said.

"Oh! I know exactly where that is!" she squealed.

He got up from his aching knees and said, "Well, why don't you just *show* me?"

He told me that what happened next truly amazed him. "Dan, I never figured she'd have a better method of finding leaks in those buried copper lines than I did—but she did."

And here's how she did it. She got herself a mop and a bucket. She filled the bucket halfway with water from the kitchen sink, and then she soaked the mop. She took the damp mop and ran it back and forth across the floor, and then she stood back and said, "Watch!"

"And while I watched, Dan, the pipes appeared like magic as the water dried on the floor," he told me. "And the leak appeared as a *circle*, but the pipes appeared as *long lines*! And I stood there, humbled by the common sense of this woman who lived in that house.   She had taught me a thing or two about troubleshooting, and I was feeling a bit dumb. All those years I was crawling around with a screwdriver, and all the time I could have been using a mop."

I wrote a story about the Mop Lady once and received a letter from an old-timer who asked me what I would have done with a room that had a rug. "What do you do with the bedrooms and the living room, Jerky?" the guy wrote. I gave it some consideration, and then I gave up. I called him and told him I didn't have an answer for a room with a rug.

"You ain't so smart," he said.

"Tell me something I don't know," I said.

"Cats!" he said.

"Cats?" I asked.

"Cats!" he said again. "We used cats in the old days to find the leaks under the rugs. You ever watch a cat walk around a room?" he asked.

"Not really," I said.

"Well, you should, Jerky, because a cat will always lay down on the warmest spot it can find. And if it's wandering around a radiantly heated floor, and if there's a hole in a buried pipe, the average cat will find it within a few minutes. That's why we used them. They are *excellent* leak detectors.

So I learned something about cats and common sense. I also learned that in this business, it doesn't matter if they call you "Jerky"—so long as they teach you something shortly thereafter.

You ever go to a poultry farm where they heat the chicks with a radiant floor? Those chicks stand on top of the pipes like soldiers lining up for inspection. You can tell exactly where the pipes are, and where the leaks are. Mops, cats, chicks, and common sense. You know everything you need to know, pal. You're just not sure that you know it. But that's changing pretty quickly, isn't it?

An installer remembers

John Mitchell, who now lives in California, once installed radiant heat in Levittown. Here's what he recalls.

"In 1946, no one was an expert in the design and application of radiant heat for slab homes. In Levittown, the first few models had radiant heat, but none of us knew how deep in the slab the copper tubes should be. Also, when the models first opened, there was deep snow on the ground. None of us had thought to insulate the sides of the slabs. Radiant heat, we learned, goes not only upward, but also laterally! The snow around the slabs melted three feet out from each house. We watched as crocuses bloomed all around the slabs—in the dead of winter. I remember one of the real estate salesmen saying, 'What a deal! The owners can have flowers growing all year around.'

"I also recall how we made up the coils. We called them "trombones" because the bent copper resembled the slide of a brass trombone. With Bill Levitt's help, we were able to get 1/2" soft copper in long lengths, and large quantities. We had our shop turn out several wooden drums that were about six inches high, and of various diameters 6" 8" & 10". We also had them make us a 2"x12" plank with a center pivot, set up on a stand made of two-by-fours, so that we could turn it like a merry-go-round. We drilled the plank at the three-, four-, and five-foot point on either side of the pivot point so that we could bend the copper into six, eight-, and ten-foot lengths. We manually bent the copper into figure-8 loops, and once we had bent enough of them, we bundled them and sent them to the site. On site, all we had to do was spread out the trombones and solder the two ends into the main hot water line. I know it sounds complicated, but it went in pretty easily.

"There was one thing about the concept of radiant in those early days that was really interesting. The buyers were, for the most part, young people who never questioned the type of heating system they were getting. Most of these buyers had grown up in the apartment buildings of New York City. They were used to having steam heat. They were so starry-eyed about owning their first home that nothing really bothered them—until their mothers came to visit. The old gals were so used to sticking their butts up against those steam radiators! "Now, that's heat!" they'd say. It was very hard to convince the mothers that heat coming from the floor would be good for their children and grandchildren. On follow-up visits to the new Levittown homes, I constantly heard young homeowners say, 'My mother says we'll burn our feet and the kids will get blistered when they play on the floor.'

"It was tough selling to people who were used to other types of heat!"

Here's hoping it's won't be so tough for you.

How I came to *love* Levittown

I was sixteen years old the winter I first laid down on Maureen's living room floor. It was December, and the north wind blustered through the carport and rattled the storm windows, as it so often does on Long Island.

Her mother, whom it occurs to me now was younger than I am today, sat in the kitchen, not ten feet away. She sipped a cup of black coffee, smoked an unfiltered Pall Mall, and stared intently out the window and onto the frozen front lawn. She was, I know now, listening to our quietness.

There was a brick fireplace in the center of the house with a hearth that opened onto both the living room and the kitchen. I could see her mother's legs across the andirons. Her slippered feet tapped to the rock-and-roll music coming from the black-and-white TV. We were watching either Hullabaloo or Shindig.

William Levitt, I learned years later, had built nearly 50,000 houses like this one in New York and Pennsylvania during the days that followed World War II. Each house had a hydronic, radiant-floor heating system. I didn't know it then, but small, copper pipes lay buried in the floor beneath Maureen and me. Warm water flowed from a squat boiler that sat next to their fireplace in the kitchen. It coursed through those tiny pipes an inch below us, and passed its heat into the tons of concrete that made up the floor. The boiler had a white enameled cover, and I remember thinking that it was a washing machine. Shows you what I knew.

"You two all right in there?" Maureen's mother asked, leaning down to shoot us a look through the hearth. I jerked reflexively, widening the gap between her daughter and myself.

"Everything's fine, mom," Maureen said. "Just fine!"

"Fine, fine!" I parroted, folding my arms across my chest, and scooting a few inches further away from her daughter.

"Can you turn that TV down?" her mother said, more a command than a request. "I can't hear a thing."

"Sure, mom."

"And you two should sit on the *couch*," she ordered, which we did immediately. "It's more comfortable on the *couch*."

It wasn't, of course. I *hated* getting up off that floor. It was so *good* down there. It was like lying on the beach in July. So incredibly warm!

In those days, I knew nothing about hydronic radiant heating. My father was in the plumbing supply business, and we had hydronic heat in our house, but we didn't have hydronic *radiant* heat. We weren't lucky enough to have those radiant floors. Our house just didn't *feel* the same as Maureen's. Maureen's floor tugged at me. It was the *best* place to be. To this day, I associate hydronic radiant heating with all good things: warmth, comfort, young love, and, of course . . . *mother*hood.

"Aren't you two uncomfortable?" she said. "Look, you're all squashed on that one couch cushion. Spread out. Give yourself some more room."

We did, of course.

The Sixties came and went and, in 1972, I married The Lovely Marianne. We moved into our first apartment, which was in a brand-new building out on Long Island. This place had what we came to know as a scorched-air heating system. Its memory perches dark and dusty in my mind.

That cursed furnace would belch dry, overheated air down on our newlywed bodies from morning until night. The thermostat would swing wildly, trying to keep up, but it was *never* comfortable in that first apartment. Within weeks of moving in, we began to have unexplained bloody noses and more colds than young healthy people should be having.

After putting up with this for three frigid winters, we finally figured it out and made a decision. We had to get away from scorched-air heat.

We broke our lease and The Lovely Marianne found us a new place near where we had both grown up. To my delight, it turned out to be the upstairs of a Levitt house. Our new place was a carbon copy of Maureen's old house, and those feelings of toasty comfort came flowing back into my stuffed-up head. We couldn't wait to move in.

There would, however, be some challenges. First, we lived upstairs, not downstairs. Instead of warm floors, we had baseboard convectors. I didn't think convectors were as good as warm floors, but they were a huge improvement over that nasty scorched-air system.

The second challenge was a bit tougher. The landlord (who took his rent checks at a post office box) would often neglect to pay the Oil Company, so the Oil Company would, in turn, neglect to deliver the oil.

I can remember seeing Marianne's frosty breath on more than one icy morning. And when that happened, I'd walk downstairs and knock on Al and Kathy's door. Al and Kathy, who together weighed over 600 pounds, rented the downstairs of the Levitt house. They didn't know where the landlord lived either.

"What's up?" Al would ask.

"The heat's off again," I'd say.

"C'mon in," he'd answer. "I didn't know it was off."

Al and Kathy never knew the heat was off because they had the radiant floors. Their place stayed warm long after the boiler had sucked up the last drop of oil from the tank. Al and Kathy were perfectly comfortable.

As I told you before, when it comes from a concrete floor, hydronic radiant heat can do that. The floor gets warm, and it then holds the heat and releases it as you need it. The colder it gets outside, the more heat the floor gives up. And in those days, even though there was no oil to burn, the floor still sat there and glowed softly.

"I can't get hold of the landlord," I said. "We have to call the Oil Company and get some oil. Do you have any money to lay out?"

"I don't have any money," Al would say, shrugging his beefy shoulders. Al *never* had any money. He spent it all on food. So while we tried to reach the landlord, I'd scratch up some money and call the Oil Company. As we waited for the delivery, Al and Kathy would sit in blissful comfort on their warm slab of concrete while we froze upstairs.

From that winter of my youth when I first fell in love with a warm floor, I have always associated hydronic radiant heat with the good stuff in life, and *that's* why I want to help you bring it back. We've never needed it more than we do right now.

CHAPTER 5

. . . .

The 30–Year Hiatus

Strangely, it was a ribbon of roads that caused hydronic radiant heat to take a 30-year hiatus in America. On November 29, 1944, the United States Congress passed the Federal Highway Act establishing the idea of a new national system of interstate highways. They planned to have 40,000 miles of roads connect 42 state capitals and serve 182 of the 199 U.S. cities with populations over 50,000. Twelve years later, on June 29, 1956, Congress passed the Federal Aid Highway Act. This act appropriated the money and authorized the actual construction of what was to become a 42,500-mile network of roads linking the major U.S. urban centers (the Feds picked up 90 percent of the $33.5 billion price tag). The new legislation indirectly subsidized trucking firms, intercity bus lines, motor vehicle producers, and oil companies. It left railroads unsubsidized and allowed them to depreciate and abandon their unprofitable passenger services. The system was supposed to be completed by 1972, but that date proved to be unrealistic. By 1976, though, they had finished 38,000 miles, which is pretty remarkable, don't you think?

The first thing people did when the highways came was to get in their cars and leave the cities for the suburbs. Builders accommodated these folks by throwing up millions of homes. The builders worked quickly, and they built cheaply because the market was so competitive. The builders chose to use scorched air because a furnace will always be cheaper than a boiler.

The Hydronics Institute, an organization made up of boiler and radiator manufacturers, tried to compete with the furnace folks. They ran classes they called I=B=R Schools (I=B=R stands for Institute of Boiler and Radiation Manufacturers), and they fell in love with high-temperature hydronics. In their 1966 Installation Guide for Residential Hydronic Heating Systems, they wrote,

The output of a heat distribution unit increases when there is an increase in average water temperature. If a 215-degree design water temperature is selected, the heat distributing units will be smaller than if a lower design water temperature were selected. For example, the size of heat distribution units required at a design water temperature of 170-degrees F, will be nearly 60 percent larger than when a design water temperature of 215-degrees F is used.

In other words, if you make the water hotter, you can make the radiators smaller and cheaper. You can also make the pipes smaller because the water will take a greater temperature drop as it travels around the system (if you design it that way).

There was this one difficulty, though, and my friend Jim Roche once explained it in a very funny way. Jim is a trainer for the Burnham Corporation, and one of the most experienced guys around when it comes to hydronic heating. Here's what he had to say about high-temperature hydronics at a seminar I attended.

I've always loved cast iron baseboard because of its radiant effect. Unfortunately, it cost more than I could afford when I was younger. To get around the price in my first house, I decided to use

*half as much and run it at higher temperature, as the I=B=R peo-
ple were suggesting. I designed the system for 247 degrees F, and
I installed it.*

*The first thing I noticed was that the copper tubing connecting
the baseboard changed color. We could smell paint burning for three
years after the installation. We couldn't touch the kids' toys if they
got within a foot of the baseboard. In fact, the kids would break balloons on the baseboard every time we had a birthday party. It was-
n't the easiest thing in the world to live with.*

So if you don't want the little ones to reach their kindling
point and burst into flames, I would suggest you avoid high-
temperature hydronics for home heating. There's also this difficulty with convective currents. When the water's that hot, it
makes the heated air rocket up toward the ceiling. That increases your body's heat loss through convection. It moves more
dust around, and if the house isn't immaculate, it causes
"streaking" on the walls as the dirt from the floor attaches itself
to the walls.

When hydronic radiant heating began to grow again in
America it did so because a group of European marketers decided we were finally ready for what they had been enjoying for
quite a while, that being *low*-temperature hydronics. When it
comes to hydronic heating, particularly hydronic *radiant* heating, the Europeans have been ahead of us for years. They are a
very smart group of people, and we can learn *lots* of good stuff
from them.

How the Europeans got so smart so fast

They sell gasoline by the liter in Europe. I figure some
shrewd marketer came up with that idea to make the price seem
a bit less ridiculous. Gasoline and heating fuels don't come
cheaply over there.

"Why so expensive?" I once asked a German heating engineer.
"The taxes!" he said. "We pay about three times for fuel

what you pay in America. It makes us think all the time about conservation."

Remember the gas lines of the 1970s? While waiting on those lines, I used to think about solar collectors, pipe coils for the fireplace, multi-fuel boilers, low-water-content boilers, stack dampers, and setback thermostats. All of that stuff was new back then. The spiraling price of fuel inspired this rush of invention. Remember? But then the prices stabilized and, let's face it; we pretty much stopped thinking about conservation. Not so in Europe, though. Because of the heavy taxes, their prices stabilized *three times higher* than ours did. That kept everyone's attention focused on conservation. And it spurred even *more* invention, which is what made them so good. Those folks were *inspired*!

What allowed the Europeans to jump so quickly into low-temperature hydronics was a product that had arrived in the nick of time. It took years to develop, but it showed up when it was needed. That product was PEX, and here's how it came to be.

In 1939, a group of English chemists were studying the reaction between ethylene and benzaldehyde. They were cooking this brew in an autoclave under an extremely high pressure. Suddenly, the autoclave exploded and destroyed most of the laboratory. Fortunately, no one was hurt.

When the scientists crept back into the lab and looked inside what was left of the autoclave, they found a white waxy substance. No one knew what this stuff was at first, but further study of the molecular structure revealed it was a gas that, having been subjected to such high pressure, had turned into a solid!

They called it "polyethylene," and then for the next several years tried to make it again. Finally, they succeeded by duplicating the original experiment, which means they blew up another laboratory. This is what is known as The Scientific Method.

Anyway, from this they learned that it was the sudden introduction of *oxygen* that made the chemical marriage possible.

Needless to say, they quickly found a safer and less costly way to introduce oxygen. Polyethylene went on to play a major role in World War II and the laying of undersea cables.

Today, polyethylene is a really popular material. We use it to move cold water and even natural gas. It's flexible in both hot and cold temperatures. It's resistant to chemicals. It doesn't scratch easily and it's smooth on the inside so fluids flow though it very easily. Polyethylene is what engineers call a "thermoplastic," which means it gets hard when it's cold and soft when it's hot. When it gets to 300 degrees F, polyethylene melts, so this thermoplastic characteristic was a challenge. Polyethylene starts to get mushy when you run hot water through it.

Scientists experimented for years with its molecular structure, trying to get the molecules to join together, or "crosslink," in a three-dimensional fashion. They figured that if they could do this, they would have a new material that would be able to take much more stress as well as higher temperatures. In short, they were looking for a material that kept all the good characteristics of polyethylene, but left out that mushy quality.

Thomas Engel, a Swedish scientist, finally succeeded in the late 1960s. He created what we today call PEX (or crosslinked polyethylene). Because of its unique molecular structure, PEX can withstand 200-degree water, even when under pressure. And this resilient plastic always returns to its original shape. You can heat it and cool it as often as you like; it always "remembers" what it's supposed to look like. It's pretty smart stuff! If you make pipe from PEX and the pipe gets a kink in it, you can just heat the pipe and, because it is PEX, it will remember its original shape and return to it as soon as it cools. I'll bet *you* couldn't do that.

Professor Engel brought his discovery to many chemical companies but none had any idea what to do with it. Finally, the Professor's neighbor, a chicken farmer, asked him if he could make pipes out of this new material. The farmer thought that if he could lay this rustproof pipe in the ground under his hens, they would feel warmer and lay more eggs. Recalling this, Professor Engel said years later, "If a shoe factory had been present in my vicinity at that time, we would perhaps today all be walking around on shoe soles made of crosslinked polyethylene."

But that's not what happened. Professor Engel took his material to the Swedish pipe manufacturer, Wirsbo, and they made *pipes* from it. They installed some under the grass of a stadium at the Munich Olympics in 1972 and got lots of attention. Then the OPEC oil embargo of 1973 took us all by surprise, and the price of oil went berserk. People, particularly European people, began to take a second look at hydronic radiant heat because it operates at a much lower cost than any other type of central heating system. They remembered those British systems of the 1930s and 1940s and figured that if it worked then, it will also work now.

And this is why you can now find so many warm floors and smiling faces in Europe.

Low-temperature hydronics returns

Before the Energy Crisis, many Europeans heated their homes with freestanding cast iron radiators. They used high-temperature water, and their systems were just like the ones we were installing in America. When the oil embargo came, European engineers realized they could save money if they lowered the temperature of the water. Of course, they'd have to make their radiators bigger to compensate for the lower water temperature.

Since PEX had arrived on the scene, it made things a lot easier. PEX pipe could withstand more stress than copper tubing or steel pipe. It was corrosion proof. It was easy to work with, and it allowed the Europeans to use the entire floor as a radiator. That gave them the "big radiator" they needed to compensate for the lower temperature water their new systems needed.

To compete with the radiant-floor manufacturers, a number of European radiator manufacturers began to make their radiators larger so they, too, could heat a room with low-temperature water. They made these radiators from steel because that gave them more flexibility in design than cast iron. These radiators quickly began to take on unusual shapes and colors. Maybe they had to be big, but that didn't mean they had to be ugly.

Today, a European contractor can select radiators that are available in the shape of benches, room dividers, towel racks, stair railings, mirrors, and even animals! One company, Zender (Runtal is their American subsidiary), produces nearly three-quarters of a million radiators a year in any of 400 colors. That represents about 20% of the total European radiator market. If you want, they'll hand-paint a portrait of your spouse, or your dog, or your cat, or whatever you desire on their flat panel radiators. They'll even gold plate one for you if you have the bucks. Not only do these new radiators get the job done beautifully; they also become a part of the decor.

To save fuel, Europeans began to lower the design temperatures of their hydronic systems. The larger, panel-type radiators had no difficulty warming rooms with these lower temperatures. In 1972, one year before the first OPEC oil embargo, the standard was to supply water to the radiators at 195 degrees F, and return it to the boiler at 160 F. Notice how they worked with a 35-degree temperature drop across the system. In America, we have always embraced the 20-degree temperature drop because, even though it makes the pipes bigger, it makes the math easier. If you're working with a 20-degree temperature drop and you want to know the flow rate, all you have to do is divide the I=B=R Heating Capacity of the boiler by 10,000 to get your answer. The Europeans with their 35-degree temperature drop would have to divide by 17,500 to get the flow rate. Which you'll have to admit is a bit tougher to do in your head.

The water temperatures dropped pretty quickly once fuel prices went up. Design temperatures went from a high of 195 degrees F in 1972 to a required temperature difference of 175 F (out) and 145 F (back). They lowered that not long after to

160 – 125, and then again to 140 – 115. At the lower temperature, panel radiators get very close to providing the same sort of comfort you feel when you walk into a room heated by a hydronic radiant floor. There's very little convective movement of air because the water inside the panel radiator isn't that hot.

If you're heating a home and you use a mixture of hydronic radiant floors and panel radiators you will be *very* pleased with the results. Low temperature is *definitely* the way to go.

Hydronic radiant systems *love* low-temperature boilers

The Europeans have been teaching us a lesson in hydronics for a while now. We've learned that low-temperature systems operate more economically and provide better levels of comfort than high-temperature systems. The one challenge with a low-temperature system, though, is that the boiler's relatively cold, water-to-fire, heat-transfer surfaces can make the flue gases reach their dew point and condense into a nasty acidic brew. Those condensed gases can eat holes in boilers, burners and flue pipes.

To get around this, the Europeans developed new types of boilers that can take relatively cold water without causing the flue gases to condense. I recently heard that one of these Euro-boilers got hit with a 20-degree F antifreeze solution from a snow melt system while at full fire (unintentionally, of course). That boiler survived the shock, and I think that's pretty impressive, don't you?

To operate under low-water-temperature conditions, these boilers use a special design that separates the fire from the relatively cold return water. It may be a sort of air gap built into the boiler, a "thermal pane window" between the cold water and the hot gases, if you will. The inside of a thermal pane window doesn't collect moisture because it's insulated from the cold outside surface by a layer of trapped gas, right? You can do a similar thing with a boiler if you design it well. Another manufacturer has the cold return water flowing through a pipe that's built into the center of the boiler. The hot boiler water preheats this cold return water before the return water has a chance to touch the boiler's actual water-to-fire heat transfer surfaces.

These boilers are somewhat larger, and contain more water, than the boilers we've seen coming from US boiler manufacturers lately. Europeans insist that their high-water-content boilers operate at higher overall combustion efficiency. Some US boiler manufacturers say you save money with a low-water-content boiler because there's less water to heat on each firing cycle. The argument has been going on for a couple of decades now, and contractors have pretty much made up their minds as to what works best for them.

As I see it, the high-water-content boiler *will* operate at better overall efficiency for reasons that are pretty simple. If the heat loss of a house on a particular day during the winter is, say, 60,000 BTUH, that's all the heat the boiler will need to put into the house. The burner will run until some control shuts it off. That's a fact of life. Another fact is that the longer the burner is on, the better its overall combustion efficiency will be. This is because burners are not that efficient when they first start, and later when they stop. That's why you should beware of the short cycling that comes along with an oversized boiler. Not only does the constant on-and-off action of the burner make your customers angry, it also costs them money and shortens the life of the system components.

So if the house needs 60,000 BTUH, that's all the boiler will put in. The boiler may have to run a total of, say, 20 minutes out of an hour to give the house that much heat. If you have a high-water-content boiler, it may run for two, ten-minute cycles during that hour. If you have a low-water-content boiler, however, it may operate five times during that hour, each time burning for four minutes. Both boilers would have put 60,000 BTUH into the house, but the high-water-content boiler would have been more efficient while it was running because its cycles were longer. Think about it. And don't oversize your boilers.

That, in plain English, is what you get with the bigger European-style boilers — that and their ability to handle cold return water. If you ask an engineer from the boiler manufacturer to explain what I just told you, he will show you charts that look like maps of downtown Boston and make you crazy with numbers and scientific formulas. Those guys are not the best communicators in the world. Just remember, the longer the burner runs, the better the combustion efficiency will be. Got it?

There are also condensing boilers that burn natural gas and turn the flue gases into liquid. The liquid then runs down the drain (in Europe, they first neutralize the pH with filters so they don't kill the plants and wildlife). Condensing boilers are perfect for radiant systems since the relatively cool return water causes the flue gases to do what you want them to do, that being turn to liquid. The more heat you can suck out of the flame, the more efficient the boiler will be. But you're *not* supposed to condense with a non-condensing boiler.

Many of these condensing boilers are low-water-content boilers. These companies have figured out how to put *both* low-water-content and extremely high combustion efficiency together.

Condensing boilers make the most sense in radiant systems, but if you use them in a high-temperature system, the gases won't condense as readily, which defeats the purpose of the boiler's design.

One manufacturer, Dunkirk, makes a boiler they call the Quantum Leap. This is a natural gas, condensing boiler that continues to condense the gases even in high-temperature (180-degree) systems. It's a unique boiler, and well worth checking out.

Now that I've explained a lot of the history and the theory, let's take a look at what goes on out in the field. Let's say some homeowner watches *This Old House* on TV. She sees Richard Trethewey installing radiant heat and she's interested. She calls and asks you to stop by and take a look at her home. "Can you install radiant heat for me?" she asks.

Here's what you need to do next.

C H A P T E R 6

. . . .

As You Approach the Job

When they were building Levittown, the Dead Men followed some simple rules of thumb that the Institute of Boiler and Radiation Manufacturers (I=B=R) had set up. These rules of thumb grew out of the experience manufacturers such as the Chase Brass & Copper Company had had. I=B=R also had a house at the University of Illinois where they tested many new types of hydronic systems. The rules for radiant back then were simple, and there's no reason why they have to be complicated nowadays.

Here are some examples of those old rules of thumb. This is from the *I=B=R Installation Guide Number 6, Panel Heating for Small Structures*, which the Institute published in August 1951. The notes in italic are from me to you.

1. Boilers should be automatically fired. The control of water temperature in hand-fired installations is not close enough for panel heating. *(Remember, they were writing this at a time when many systems still burned coal.)*

2.   Slab floors, whether or not they are used as a heating panel, must be provided with at least one-inch-thick, waterproof edge insulation that is buried at least 24 inches deep, or to the bottom of the frost line.   The use of a waterproof membrane (vapor barrier) between the gravel fill and the slab is recommended. *(This is the advice that William Levitt didn't follow when he built Levittown.)*

3.   All pits should be provided with drains. *(They put their distribution manifolds in pits they left in their concrete floors. These weren't deep pits; they just built small squares from scrap wood before they poured the concrete and set manifolds below grade.   They brought supply and return connections to their manifolds from the boiler. The buried tubing connected to the other side of the manifolds. They wanted drains so the manifolds wouldn't go under water and corrode.)*

4.   Where panels do not cover the entire area of the floor or ceiling, the coil should be located near the exposed perimeter of the room. *(If you have to make a choice, it's always best to put your tubing near the coldest surfaces.)*

5.   All pipes ends should be reamed. *(By reaming the pipes, they reduced the frictional resistance to flow and got to use the smallest circulators possible.)*

6.   Connections between circulator and boiler should be as close as possible. *(Again, this was to keep the friction as low as possible.)*

7.   Whenever the size of pipe changes in a horizontal run, use an eccentric reducer, keeping the topside level. *(Did you figure this one out? An eccentric reducer has one flat side that follows the plane of the larger pipe. By keeping that flat side on the top, they lessened the chance that trapped air would gather there. In a steam system, the Dead Men used eccentric reducers between pipes of dif-*

ferent sizes, but they put the flat part on the bottom so the conden-sate couldn't form a puddle that might lead to water hammer.)

8.   Drains should be installed at all low points. *(So they could drain the system and prevent freeze-ups if they weren't using antifreeze.)*

9.   All high points should be vented. Vents should also be installed where the plane of the system changes. *(This was to help them get rid of the air on start-up.)*

10.   Balancing cocks or valves should be used on each coil. They should be installed below traffic plates for floor panels, and with extended stems, if necessary, for ceiling plates. *(By increas-ing the resistance to flow through the shorter circuits, the Dead Men were able to trick the water into thinking there was no path of least resistance in the system. They wanted to keep the handles acces-sible so they could fine-tune the system to the customer's comfort needs later on.)*

11.   A mixing or tempering valve should be used to control the temperature of the water to the heating system if the boiler is also used to supply domestic hot water. This valve should be connected in accordance with the valve manufacturer's recom-mendations. *(A mixing valve was a big improvement over that $^3/_4$" x $^1/_8$" bushing Mr. Levitt used to control the temperature on his sys-tems. Remember, there was only one heating zone on these early jobs; the installer maintained 180-degree water in the boiler for the tankless coil, and tempered the supply water by mixing cool return water into the "cold" side of the mixing valve. They fed boiler water into the mixing valve's "hot" side, and directed the "mixed" port's flow back out toward the radiant panel.)*

12.   A flow control valve should be used when the heating panels are above the boiler and the boiler is used also to supply domestic hot water. *(This was to keep hot boiler water from migrat-*

*ing by gravity circulation into the radiant panel when the circulator
was off. If the panel was below the boiler, which it usually was, they
saved the money on the flow-control valve because hot water is less
likely to migrate downward since it's lighter than the cold water that's
already down in the panel.)*

13. A pressure relief valve should be installed on the boiler.
*(To keep the boiler from winding up in the next county, should things
not go as planned.)*

14. The air cushion tank should be located above the boiler.
*(The compression tank is what they're talking about here. This was
in the days before the diaphragm-type compression tank came along
and took over. They put the steel compression tank higher than the
boiler so the air that separated from the water had a chance to rise
into the tank. They often used special devices such as the Bell &
Gossett Airtrol fittings to catch the air and direct it toward the tank.)*

15. Coils should be filled with water very slowly in order to
vent them properly.   *(They had lots of little pipes heading in all
directions. They wanted to make sure they got the air from each one.
If they filled them too quickly, air might stay in one circuit while the
water bypassed through another circuit, giving the impression back
in the boiler room that water had filled the entire system.)*

16. The entire piping system should be tested to a hydrostatic pressure of 100 psi for a minimum of four hours before being
connected to the boiler and before being concealed. *(The time to
find any leaks is <u>before</u> you pour the concrete. Hydrostatic, in case
you don't know, means "water that's at rest.")*

17. Because of variable conditions, controls should be selected and installed in accordance with control manufacturers' recommendations. *(Every job is different, right? Talk to the controls
manufacturer. This is <u>still</u> good advice!)*

For <u>Floor</u> Panel Systems:

18. Coils should not be laid on, nor come in contact with, cinders or other corrosive fill. *(In the days when everyone burned coal, they had to find a place to put all that ash. A lot of it wound up as fill on construction sites. They didn't want the metal pipe touching this stuff because it would eat right through the pipes and cause leaks. If the ground contained corrosive fill, and they couldn't avoid it, they would trench for the pipes and fill the trenches with crushed limestone. Limestone is alkaline; it counteracts the acid in the ashes. And by the way, now you know where the term "cinder block" comes from.)*

19. Coils should start 6" from the exposed perimeter of a floor slab. Use ³/₄" tube or pipe on 12" centers with 120-degree F water. This will deliver 50 BTUH per square foot of panel. *(This was the classic rule of thumb for placing tubing. They started them 6" from the exposed perimeter to keep the carpenters from driving nails through the hydronic tubing when the base plates were going down. They went for 50 BTUH per square foot because most folks had thick rugs on their floors. Nowadays, the standard is 35 BTUH per square foot, maximum, for bare floors. That's the most you can put into the floor and still keep the surface temperature from exceeding 85 degrees F.)*

For <u>Ceiling</u> Panel Systems:

20. All ceiling panels should be backed by insulation whether or not there is a heated space above. When panels are exposed to an unheated space, at least 3-⁵/₈" rock wool insulation or equivalent is recommended. Use nominal ³/₈" tube on 6" centers with 140-degree water. This will deliver 60 BTUH per square foot of panel. *(See how they used hotter water in ceiling panels? They could do this because no one walks on the ceiling. If your feet don't touch it, it can be hotter. The tubing was smaller so they wouldn't need to use as much plaster on the ceiling. You should always have insula-*

tion on the "other side" of a radiant panel to keep the heat from going the wrong way.)

21. For ceiling panels it is advisable to design the coils so that the tube runs at right angles to the joists, which will give better support. *(For obvious reasons, right?)*

22. Coils should start 3" from the exposed perimeter of a ceiling. *(Again, this is to keep the carpenters from nailing through the tubes when they put up their molding.)*

23. Coils in ceiling panels should not be used to dry the plaster. The first time heat is applied in a new installation, the temperature of the coils should be raised only a few degrees F each day. *(To keep the ceiling from cracking and falling down on your noggin.)*

See? Hydronic radiant heat never was that complicated. You know everything you need to know! It doesn't have to be complicated nowadays either. Just keep using your common sense as we move on here. This next part is *really* important.

Watch out!

When you're checking out a job where the folks are considering hydronic radiant heat, there are a few things that should catch your attention like bright red flags. These are potential sources of trouble, so beware.

Three walls of glass Be careful around those rooms that have glass on three sides. The heat loss in a room such as this will be greater than it will be in a room that has glass on just one or two sides. Remember that you have just so much floor space available and you can only get so many BTUH per square foot of floor space if you want to avoid overheating the surface of the floor. If the floor gets too hot, so will the feet and that's when people become unhappy.

I ran computerized heat loss calculations on what I'd consider to be two, typical, 20' X 20' rooms of standard construction. The only things I varied between the two were the windows. In the first room, I sized the heat loss based on having windows on two sides. The heat loss was 14,976 BTUH. In the second room, I added windows to a third wall and the heat loss jumped by 21 percent to 18,924. If you don't have enough floor space to provide that additional BTUH output, the room probably won't be comfortable on the coldest days of the year. You'll have to supplement that room with additional heat. For instance, you might have to put some tubing in the ceiling or the lower walls.

Prevailing winds over 15 mph The house you're looking at might be in a place where the wind blows all the time, and if it is, be careful. The wind can weasel its way into cracks in the house and create drafts. If the house is near the ocean or up on top of a hill, take note and figure that into your heat loss calculation. A hydronic radiant heat loss calculation will always be less than a convective heat loss calculation (such as the standard I=B=R, ACCA Manual J, or ASHRAE calculations). One of the reasons for this is that a radiant heat loss calculation pretty much ignores heat loss by infiltration. This is because a hydronic radiant system makes the air inside the house very still. Still air is less likely to promote infiltration because there's no air moving past the windows and doors. When the wind is howling, this can change, and you'll have to compensate when you're figuring the heat loss. If you don't know how to do a radiant heat loss calculation, just be sure to tell the person who is going to do the calculation that Mr. Breezy is present and hard at work.

Rooms with lots of stone People who camp out in the woods on cold nights have a trick that helps them keep warm. They'll put a couple of big stones in the campfire and when they're ready to turn in for the night they'll take the stones from the fire (YEOW!), and lay them inside the tent. The stones suck up lots of BTUs while they're in the fire, which they then slowly release inside the tent. If the camper keeps the flaps closed, those stones will keep the inside of the tent toasty until dawn.

Remember what I told you earlier about the Levittown houses? Those concrete slabs stayed warm for days, even though the power lines were down. Rocks hold heat. That's why you should be careful with your control strategy when you're working with a room that has brick or stone walls or big fireplaces. These rooms will take a bit longer to heat, and they'll stay warmer long after the water stops flowing through the tubing. They're best left on their own zone.

High-hat lights Because the standard ones have no insulation, high-hat lights can suck the heat right out of a room and stick it into a ventilated attic. They can add considerably to a room's heat loss, which is why you have to ask about them when you're checking out the job. Imagine what the heat loss through this one will be on a cold winter's day.

Several manufacturers make insulated high-hats that cost just a few bucks more than the standard type but create less heat loss. I know you're not the electrician, but it makes you look great when you mention things such as this to the homeowner.

Old houses You'll find more insulation between Mars and Jupiter than you'll find inside the walls of most old houses. Since the current homeowner probably won't let you punch holes in their walls when you're quoting the job, assume the worst and figure on there not being much insulation there when you do your radiant heat loss calculation. And by the way, if it's feasible, try to talk the folks into insulating the place before they spend all that money on a heating system. They'll be happier, and it will be better for you as well in the long run. Never be afraid to talk to a customer about things that cost money. How they spend their money is not your decision. Your job is to tell them what's in their best interest, and insulation is *definitely* in their best interest.

Wet wood There shouldn't be more than six percent moisture in any wood you're going to heat. If you staple hydronic radiant tubing to wet wood, you're going to get a nasty surprise when the wood dries and turns into corduroy. How do you know the moisture content of wood? You use a moisture detector. You can pick one up at a tool store. A hundred bucks will get you a real good one.

I remember talking to a contractor who installed a hydronic radiant system in a fancy house in Connecticut. The homeowner had bought a truckload of barn wood from a guy in Maine. These planks were about five thousand years old and measured something like sixteen inches wide. They were about as thick as the Manhattan Yellow Pages and wetter than Niagara Falls – just the sort of stuff you'd want for a finished floor. The homeowner had them planed and sanded and was oh so proud of them. The contractor thought nothing of them and attached his tubing to their undersides. When he started up the system, nothing happened. Concerned, but not yet panicking, the contractor raised the temperature by degrees F. Nothing happened. Growing even more concerned because the homeowner was beginning to look like a nightmare with a law firm attached, the contractor decided to go for broke. He cranked the temperature up to 220 degrees F and left it like that overnight.

When he showed up on the job the next morning, the wood plank floor looked like Disney's Space Mountain. The contractor told me that when he walked through the door the next morning the sight of the floor registered 9.5 on the Sphincter Scale.

Don't let it happen to you, pal.

Thick carpet Are they going to lay carpet? You'd better ask because you have to figure it into your heat loss calculation. Putting a carpet and pad on a floor is like putting a sweater and winter coat on your body. Both keep the heat from escaping. If there are to be rugs, you should know. If you're thinking hardwood and they're thinking Seventies Shag, what you have there is a failure to communicate—and probably a failure to collect that all-important final payment.

Allow for the higher R-value of that carpet. If you have someone else doing the calculations for you, find out that R-value and let them know. If you can, talk the folks into a thin carpet. Even Sears advertises carpet specifically for hydronic radiant floor systems. There's not much to that stuff. It's about as thick as a washcloth.

I looked at a gorgeous house in Monterey, California a while ago. The place had hydronic radiant heat and carpets that were as thick as the owner's wallet. He told me that he warned the contractor he was going to do this. The contractor listened, and sized the system for extra tubing and a hotter-than-usual water temperature. As I write these words, that homeowner has been wonderfully comfortable for 10 years. That's what you're looking for – happy people who smile upon you and recommend you to all their friends and neighbors.

Different types of heaters I once helped a contractor troubleshoot a situation that was very bizarre. He put a kick-space heater in a new kitchen. In the same room, but on the other side, he installed a recessed convector. He took great pains to size these heaters properly. On the coldest day of the year, the homeowners would need them both.

And when the coldest day of the year arrived, the homeowners were cold. They called the contractor and he got frustrated so he called me for some free advice and the only thing I could figure was that those two types of heaters weren't getting along. The recessed convector wanted the air at the floor level to be cold so it could grab it, heat it, and send it up toward the ceiling. The kick-space heater, however, kept heating the air and launching it across the floor before it could go sailing upward toward the ceiling. On its way across the floor, the heated air was interfering with the cold air the recessed convector needed. The result was the recessed convector did nothing. Water flowed through it, but the temperature didn't drop by much, which meant the air wasn't removing the heat. The contractor knew this was true because he had installed thermometers just about everywhere during the days when he was losing his mind and pulling out his hair.

I mention this because you have to know that some heaters won't work well with others. You *must* remember this when you're doing a radiant heat loss calculation. Those figures depend on the air in the room being still. That's one of the reasons why the total required BTUH is relatively low. Remember we talked about this before? If you put in any sort of blower that creates convective currents in the room, you might not have enough heat on the coldest day of the year. Please keep this in mind.

And stay away from those ceiling fans if you're doing hydronic radiant heat in a room with a high ceiling. It makes no sense to be moving that relatively cool air around during the winter.

Go figure!

Heating professionals don't guess. Nor do they use the rules of thumb their grandparents swore by. They use computers and easy-to-understand software to figure out exactly what they'll need to get the job done. And if they don't have a computer or the time to use one, professionals have the good sense to find someone who does. That someone is usually the hydronic equipment manufacturer, or his rep, or the wholesaler. Pick one; they're all over the place nowadays, and they're more than willing to help.

Don't guess. Your price will be too high.

Be a professional. Your customers will love you and tell everyone they meet of your legendary prowess.

Don't guess. You'll sleep better at night.

Hydronic radiant heating systems use less energy than any other type of central heating system. I'll keep saying that until it gets stuck in your head and you begin to repeat it to your customers. And I'm not making this up. Here, check out what Bethlehem Steel had to say in one of their publications way back in 1948:

Boiler capacity for hydronic radiant heating theoretically may be reduced as much as 30 percent below that required for a conventional radiator system designed for a compatible building, but in view of the limited possible saving on a small job, and the desirability of excess capacity for more rapid pick-up during a sharp drop in outside temperature, it is recommended that boiler sizes be based on standard heating practice.

My guess is those lads were a tad nervous back in those days. They knew this stuff saved money, and that you could use a smaller boiler, but when the boiler is already small, I suppose they figured what the heck, keep the full size. But then they continue:

In a twelve-room European school building, with one wing radiantly heated and the opposite, identical wing heated by a different method, this saving is said to have been verified by accurate measurement of heat input under extended operation.

Tests reported in this country indicate that the fuel savings are somewhat less than 30 percent, due to the tendency of the system to overrun during a sharp rise in outdoor temperature. [Our controls are so much more accurate nowadays! D.H.]

There is almost unanimous opinion among owners of radiant-heating systems that important fuel savings do result. In the rare cases where fuel costs seem abnormally high for the size of the structure, poor insulation or incorrect installation may be considered basic causes.

I told you earlier about the Canadian engineer, L.H. LaFontaine, who wrote an excellent article back in 1990 for *Heating/Piping/Air Conditioning* magazine. Here's another one of his statements that proves just how far ahead of his time he was.

Manufacturers expound the virtues of radiant heating, but they neglect to take advantage of the fact that installation costs could be substantially reduced if the systems were not oversized. For example, when sizing a warm air furnace, one usually selects a unit of sufficient capacity to take care of the peak load. This would not be necessary with radiant heating; a much smaller heating capacity could be selected.

Some suppliers and installers won't risk going against the trend. They size the heating equipment according to conventional methods. Yet they report that boilers operate very infrequently even at very low outside temperatures, which would indicate that they are oversized.

You don't need to oversize. Don't be afraid to trust your figures. If they seem small, know that that's the way they're *supposed* to be.

At absolute maximum, you'll be designing your system around a heat output of 35 BTUH per square foot of floor space. That will make the floor about 85 degrees F on the most frigid day of the year. If this heat input doesn't seem like much to you, know that some of Mr. LaFontaine's Canadian systems are running at a mere 18 BTUH per square foot, and that's in a place where the outdoor temperature drops to -29 F. And we're talking about an R-value of 20 here.

Knowing this, but realizing that you probably *still* want to be conservative, I'd like you to do this. Check out the floor space you have to work with and then divide the radiant heat loss of the space by 35 BTUH (the maximum) and see how many square feet that works out to be. For instance, let's say you have a 20' x 20' room with a radiant heat loss of 10,000 BTUH. Multiply 20' x 20' to get the available square footage. That's 400 square feet, right? Okay, now multiply 400 x 35 BTUH. That should give you 14,000 BTUH, or about 40% more than you need. You can heat this room radiantly because you have enough available floor space. In fact, in this case, you'd size for just 25 BTUH per square foot (10,000 BTUH required, divided by 400 square feet available = 25 BTUH/square foot.) Get it? Good!

Now suppose that room was just 10' x 10' but the heat loss was the same. Ten by ten gives you 100 square feet of available floor space, right? Multiply 100 x 35 BTUH/square foot. You get 3,500 BTUH, and that's all the floor can do. In this case, you can't heat the room radiantly by just using the floor. The floor simply isn't big enough.

So check it out before you do anything else. Do you have enough space available? If not, you're going to have to find some other place to put tubing. It might go into the lower portion of the walls, or up in the ceiling, or you may have to add another type of radiation to the room, and if you do, watch out for heaters that create convective currents.

Normally, you'll have enough floor space available because a radiantly heated room needs less BTUH than a room heated by convection. Where you'll run into a challenge will be in those rooms with three exposed walls and a lot of glass. Also, in kitchens where there are lots of cabinets and not much wall space.

I don't think you should install radiant heat under kitchen cabinets because it makes the potatoes and carrots and onions grow. Also, a kitchen cabinet can be a *very* good insulator.

Always remember there *is* a difference.

A convective heat loss calculation is *always* going to be different from a hydronic radiant heat loss calculation because:

1. Hydronic radiant is more concerned with the heat loss of the human body than it is with the heat loss of the room.
2. With a hydronic radiant floor, the air will be nearly the same temperature at the ceiling as it is two feet above the floor. That means there will be less heat loss through the ceiling.
3. There's less air movement and, as a result, less infiltration into a house that has hydronic radiant heat.
4. Folks who sold boilers and radiators in the old days based their convective heat loss calculations on rules of thumb that were passed down from other Dead Men. They were *very* conservative because they didn't have that much experience. They arrived at their conclusions during a time when systems didn't have very many zones. That means they sized for the full-blown load, no matter what the temperature was on any particular day. Nowadays, I regularly run into contractors who will deduct 10 percent of the load, per zone, for up to four zones and never have a call back. These guys know that rarely do all the zones run at the same time. Our lifestyles are different nowadays than they were in the old days. The Dead Men also didn't have the luxury of indirect water heaters, which use idle time to make and store domestic hot water.
5. They oversized by habit. You don't have to.

Got a computer?

Trying to do business today without a computer is like trying to do business a few years ago without a truck. A computer can be like a loyal employee who works his butt off for you, but you don't have to give it benefits or a paid vacation. It's much easier to spring for the bucks when you think of it that way.

The hardware (that's the machine) is getting easier and easier to understand, and so is the software (the stuff on the floppy discs or CDs). Hydronic radiant equipment manufacturers have come up with software that can do radiant heat loss calculations in minutes, and you should get yourself a copy of that software and use it. Wirsbo and Heatway have both written excellent programs that are very popular and easy to use (I'm sure they would *love* to show you them). All you have to do is fill in the blanks and let the computer do the rest. You will consistently beat up on your competition if you act like a professional and size the job the *right* way. You will get the job done the *right* way, using less equipment. You will have the best value *every* time. You will be a bona fide Wet Head.

However, if you are thick-skulled and hell-bent on *not* getting a computer, *please* get yourself a wholesaler who is smart enough to know that he can help both you and himself get more business by using a computer. Ask for that guy's help, and then make sure you support him by buying from him. If you use the guy's services and then buy your equipment somewhere else because the other guy is a bit cheaper, you'll be doing the same thing to that wholesaler that you don't want your customer to do to you. Practice the Golden Rule, pal; it's one of those things that has passed the test of time. It works.

Rules of thumb?

A friend of mine has more than a hundred hydronic radiant jobs under his belt, and he has never had one that didn't work. Sure, some have cost him more than others because he's had to go back to fix the mistakes, but he's learned from his mistakes, and he's never made the same mistake twice. He told me he considers the cost of his mistakes to be "tuition."

He's at a point now where he can jump right into a job and just follow a rule-of-thumb recipe that works well in his part of the country. He hasn't done a heat loss calculation in quite a while; nor has he made a drawing of where the tubing should go. He just dives in and does this job pretty much the same way as he did the last job.

How does he get away with this? First, he makes sure the house is really well insulated. Next, he measures the available floor space in which he can install hydronic radiant tubing. He multiplies that by 35 BTUH per square foot. Remember I told you that was the maximum output you should ever consider because if you put in any more BTUH the floor will be hotter than 85 degrees F, which is the temperature on the outside of the clothed human bodies. Once he gets his total for the available floor space, he buys a boiler equal to that output. Does this mean his boiler is going to be oversized? Probably, because if the house is built well, it probably doesn't really need 35 BTUH per square foot. Nor will all the zones call at once. But you know what? He hasn't had a callback so he keeps doing it this way. I once asked him if his boilers operate all the time on the coldest day of the year and he laughed and told me he has *never* seen that happen. Which means he's oversizing. But that's what rules of thumb force you to do. They force you to oversize.

Next, he almost always buries his tubing either in concrete or gypsum concrete to give himself the benefit of thermal mass. He spaces the tubing on 12-inch centers throughout most of the rooms. In bathrooms, he always spaces the tubing on six-inch centers. When he comes across a window or other cold exposure he moves the tubing closer together, putting it on six-inch centers for a distance away from the wall that's equal to one-third the height of the cold exposure.

He runs his jobs on continuous circulation with outdoor reset controllers. He never uses a length of tubing that's longer than 250 feet. If any manifold has more than five circuits attached, he pipes the manifold in reverse-return, taking the supply of the first tube from the first tapping on the manifold, and returning that tube to the last tapping on the other manifold. Reverse-return, in case you don't know, means the first supplied is the last returned. That ensures an equal pressure drop across the manifold sets and makes it easier to balance the flow through the floor. Here's a photo of a manifold set piped in reverse-return.

Should my friend be using a computer to figure each job? Probably. That would save him money on equipment and increase his profit on each job, but he finds this method works well enough for him in his neighborhood, and he's been very successful. He has all the work he can handle, in fact.

I suppose he's brought back the spirit of those early days of hydronic radiant heating by using his experience to develop rules of thumb. You'll probably develop some rules of thumb of your own as you gain experience. But as you do, please remember the words of L.H. LaFontaine, that wise Canadian engineer who said, "Manufacturers expound the virtues of radiant heating, but they neglect to take advantage of the fact that installation costs could be substantially reduced if the systems were not oversized."

This also applies to the nonengineer installer. That's *you*, pal.

CHAPTER 7

. . . .

The Straight Scoop on Tubing

You have options when it comes to the tubing you bury or sta-ple up. PEX is cross-linked polyethylene – very good stuff, designed to last about 200 years, or so they tell me. You and I will never know for sure because we will be Dead Men. This is the material you'll find all over Europe where they've been doing hydronic radiant heating since the early Seventies. PEX has a great track record and has reached the point where it's almost considered a commodity item by many heating contractors and plumbers.

To avoid it becoming a commodity (which is the kiss of death for any manufacturer), PEX manufacturers have been taking the time to spell out the differences between their products. If you're wondering who makes the absolute best stuff, the answer is they *all* do. Just ask them.

Seriously though, there *are* differences in the way different companies make PEX. Most start with a material called HDPE, which stands for High-Density Polyethylene. HDPE evolved from polyethylene (the material the English scientists discovered by blowing up their laboratory, as you'll recall). PEX differs from

HDPE in that PEX has that special three-dimensional link between the molecules. Scientists actually call this stuff a "macro-molecule," meaning a 200' coil of PEX pipe comprises only a few molecules. This network is what gives PEX such a fine memory for its original shape. If you kink PEX, you can just heat it up and it will always return to the shape in which it was first crosslinked.

The linking of the molecules happens in the manufacturing process, and how the manufacturer chooses to do that affects the properties of the final product. They don't link all the molecules together because that would make the PEX too brittle. On the other hand, if they link too few molecules the material won't be any better than HDPE, from whence it came. They have to find just the right combination of linked and non-linked molecules. There are different ways to get where they need to go and, from what I've learned, some ways seem better than others. Here are the principal methods manufacturers are using today to make PEX:

Engel-method PEX (also known as PEX-A) This is the stuff Tomas Engel brought into the world. Engel-method PEX gets crosslinked while it's in its melted form. They do this by adding peroxide to the mix and then applying lots of pressure and temperature. This method gives the pipe an essentially uniform distribution of the crosslinking sites throughout the material. From what I've read in independent, scientific papers that have come from Europe, this is the best way to make PEX. It takes a while longer to do it this way and, depending on your supplier, this sort of PEX may cost a bit more.

Irradiation-method PEX (also known as PEX-C) Irradiated PEX starts out as straight polyethylene tubing. As with other methods of making straight polyethylene, the tubing takes on a definite form during the extrusion process. With the irradiation method, the crosslinking takes place in a second process where the manufacturer runs the tubing through an electron beam cannon. The beam gets the polyethylene molecules so excited that they crosslink.

This method can sometimes result in a less uniform crosslinking of the material, especially if the pipe is larger than 1" in diameter. This happens because the thicker pipe requires a higher dose of radiation. If it's not done properly, the outer layer of irradiated PEX can become brittle, but this is not a concern in a well-controlled process. If the pipe maker is experienced there is no need for concern with this sort of PEX.

Silane-method PEX (also known as PEX-B) The big difference between this method and the two others is that with the Engel and Irradiation methods, the crosslinking consists of a bond between carbon molecules. With the Silane method the crosslinking takes place across silicon and oxygen molecules. These links are weaker than the carbon-carbon links that result from the other methods, and this may have an effect on the long-term chemical stability of the material. If we live long enough, we'll probably find out.

I hope I'm not making you crazy with this chemistry business. This book, after all, is supposed to be for nonengineer installers, and all this science can get make you woozy, I know. But it's important for you to know these things because *you're* the one who's going to be burying the tubing under the floor.

In fairness, I have to tell you that none of these methods is a *bad* method; ASTM (American Society for Testing and Materials) approves them all. However, in a world among "equals," it seems to me that some are more "equal" than others. Know this when you buy; don't start thinking of PEX as a commodity item. There *is* a difference.

PEX/Aluminum/PEX I first saw this tubing in 1991 at the big ISH fair in Frankfurt, Germany. I was walking past one of the booths in the radiant heating building when a salesman handed me what looked like a plastic cane. He didn't pick me out of the crowd; he was giving canes to everyone who passed. I thought the kids would like it so I took it and twirled it like Charlie Chaplin as I continued down the aisle. But then it suddenly occurred to me that what I was twirling was hydronic radiant heat tubing (this stuff was so new to me in 1991!). I walked back to the booth and asked about it. They found someone who could speak pretty good English and he explained that this tubing had an aluminum core that was sandwiched by two layers of PEX. "The aluminum keeps out the oxygen," the representative told me. "And when you bend it, it stays bent!" This I could see as I looked at the cane. "When you put it down on the floor, it doesn't bounce back up at you." He gestured by flailing his arms.

When you put it down, it stays down. And therein lies the benefit of PEX/Aluminum/PEX. That, and the fact that it doesn't expand as much as PEX, and it has a thin aluminum, oxygen-diffusion barrier to keep oxygen from getting into the water. I'll tell you more about that in a minute.

Polybutylene I turned on my TV one Sunday night a few years ago and watched the *Sixty Minutes* team do a story on polybutylene piping. They interviewed the citizens of a town in New Mexico where the plastic plumbing systems had more leaks than a litter of puppies with bad kidneys. The difficulty was really with the fittings, not the tubing, but that didn't matter once the show aired. The public had become alert to the bad situation and that was the beginning of the end for polybutylene tubing.

Shell was the company that supplied the resin to make polybutylene and before long they were fighting a class-action lawsuit that threatened to drive them into bankruptcy. They decided to get out of the polybutylene business and that removed this tubing from consideration for those who were doing hydronic radiant heating. That's too bad because polybutylene served radiant heating contractors very well for a lot of years. It was inexpensive, flexible and versatile, but you can't get it anymore, so that's all I'm going to say about it here.

And then there's rubber

During the early 1970s when the radiant heating market was growing in Europe and PEX was coming into its own, lots of Americans were up on their roofs experimenting with solar collectors. Thanks to a friendly administration in Washington DC there was money available for all sorts of new products. Many of the early solar systems used black rubber mats to capture the sun's rays and heat domestic hot water. Out of that industry sprang a couple of companies that eventually developed products for the radiant heating market. Heatway grew to be the most prominent of these companies and today they hold a good share of the radiant heating market.

Over the years they've developed a few generations of high-tech rubber hoses that are specifically designed for radiant heating. Their earlier products did not deal with oxygen-diffusion corrosion very well, and that led to a lot of controversy, but they grew and learned and improved their product line. Today they offer a hose they call Onyx and it meets all the industry standards. It also has an aluminum oxygen-diffusion barrier, similar to the PEX/Aluminum/PEX product.

The biggest advantage the rubber products have over the plastics is flexibility. This material is as bendable as a Sears Best garden hose and it's a pleasure to work with, especially on those staple-up jobs. You can also bend it on a tighter radius and that helps if you're working in a tight space where you have to lay lots of tubing. It costs more than plastic, but you should balance that higher cost against the potential saving in labor.

A lot of installers don't care for rubber hose (fairly or unfairly) because it was at the center of the storm a few years back when everyone was talking about this oxygen-diffusion business. Here, let me tell you all about that.

What's the deal with oxygen-diffusion corrosion?

This subject was *much* more likely to start a fistfight in the early Nineties than it is nowadays. Back then, it practically broke up families! A lot of marketing was getting mixed up with the engineering in the early days of hydronic radiant heating's rebirth, and, unfortunately, many contractors became so confused they decided to ignore this wonderful equipment until the dust settled.

The dust has now settled.

Here's the straight scoop on this oxygen-diffusion corrosion business. Too much oxygen is bad for *any* hydronic system because it corrodes the iron and steel. You know this is true if you've ever lived with a boiler relief valve that keeps popping off. The oxygen in the cold fill water comes out of solution when the boiler fires and goes to work on the metals that are lowest on the metallurgical totem pole. Usually, the iron gets the worst of it. In plain English, we call this rust. You know rust, right?

Anyway, oxygen makes metals that are ferrous (that means made of iron or steel) rust. The more oxygen there is, the worse the rusting will be. Now here comes the spooky part. The wrong sort of hydronic radiant tubing can allow oxygen to pass right through it—even if it's buried under concrete. This phenomenon has nothing to do with the pressures in the system. You could have 100-psi water pressure inside the tubing and the oxygen will *still* get in – if it's the wrong sort of tubing.

Now, you may not be an engineer, but you don't *have* to be to understand this. I know you've seen a balloon or two in your day. You probably had a few at your last birthday party. Maybe you bopped one up in the air at that rock concert you went to. Balloons have more pressure inside of them than they do outside of them, right? But why do they go flat after a few days?

And how come those Mylar balloons take a lot longer to go limp? You know the sort I'm talking about? The shiny silver ones that have things like, "Over the Hill," and "Happy Birthday You Old Fart" printed on them? How come they last longer? It seems that some materials do a better job of holding gases than others, eh?

And therein lies the great answer to how the hydronic radiant tubing sucks up the oxygen. It has nothing to do with the pressure of the liquid, it has to do with the concentration of the gas we call oxygen. Mother Nature likes to balance things, and if she finds more air molecules *inside* an ordinary balloon than she finds *outside*, she will move the air molecules right through that old balloon. She can do this because an ordinary balloon is a semi-permeable membrane. That's a fancy way of saying there are tiny holes in the balloon. These holes are so tiny that liquids can't pass through them, but gases can. If you filled that balloon with water instead of air, that balloon would stay filled until the temptation to toss it at some engineer won out and you let 'er rip.

Now, follow this. When you fill a heating system with cold water, the oxygen that leaves the heated water will react chemically with the iron and steel in the system. The reaction eats up the oxygen and forms a compound called iron oxide. Iron oxide, in plain English, is rust. It's the black stuff you see suspended in the water. The longer you can leave water in an all-metal heating system (one without plastic or rubber hydronic radiant tubing) the better it gets. That's because once the oxygen reacts with the ferrous metals and forms iron oxide, the corrosion stops. That nasty, stinking, black water is like fine wine to a hydronic system. It's the *good* stuff. And as long as you don't keep adding more fresh water, you will have no more corrosion.

So here's where the tubing comes in. As soon as the oxygen burns itself up, chemically speaking, the water inside the system finds itself in oxygen deficit. In other words, there's more oxygen in the air that's *outside* the tubing than there is in the water that's *inside* the tubing. Since the tubing is a semi-permeable membrane, Mother Nature begins to shove oxygen molecules through the wall of the tubing and into the water. And that causes more corrosion. If this goes on long enough, you wind up with this sludge (rust) that flows around with the water, messing up anything that has a close tolerance to it, such as a control valve or the business end of a circulator. The oxygen also loves to go to work on the thin steel in a diaphragm-type compression tank. Oxygen won't usually damage a cast iron or steel boiler because most of these boilers have relatively large passages. The flow of water, however, will carry away the sludge and dump it in places you never even knew your system had, and that's why oxygen-diffusion corrosion is something you need to avoid.

Now, you should know that temperature plays a part in this. Generally, the hotter the water is the worse things get. If you keep the temperature below 140 F, the corrosion doesn't show itself in such a dramatic way. And since most slab installations will have the temperature of the water down around 110 degrees F, or so, oxygen-diffusion corrosion is less of a big deal. The jobs that will get you, though, are those staple-up jobs because the water will be hotter. It has to be because only a small part of the tubing touches the underside of the floor. Watch yourself on the staple-up stuff. If you're going to mess up, it will be here.

But let's get back to those balloons for a minute. How come the Mylar balloon doesn't lose its air so readily? And have you ever noticed when you're eating a bag of potato chips that the bag you're holding looks a lot like a deflated Mylar balloon?

What you have in your hand, my friend, is an example of an EVOH, which stands for a very long word I will not get into right here. An EVOH is a material that does not readily let gases through. Air can't easily get in or out. That's why the expiration date on the potato chips is something like 2055. It's also why your Mylar balloon hangs around your ceiling so long. This material is not a semi-permeable membrane.

Hydronic radiant tubing manufacturers use an EVOH that's similar to Mylar on their tubing to keep the oxygen from working its way into the water. Lately, some manufacturers have switched to a thin layer of aluminum, which they sandwich between layers of either PEX or rubber. Aluminum is a really good oxygen-diffusion barrier because it is a metal. Gases will not pass through metal. A balloon made from aluminum may not be practical, but it will *never* deflate.

If you use tubing with an oxygen-diffusion barrier such as aluminum or an EVOH coating, oxygen will not enter the tubing and you will not have any abnormal corrosion. The controversy in the early Nineties revolved around the accusation by some manufacturers that other manufacturers made tubing that did not have a suitable oxygen-diffusion barrier. They based their accusations on something called the DIN Standard. DIN, loosely translated, stands for Deutsche Industry Norm, the "Deutsche" being the Germans, who are responsible for most of the brilliance in the world of hydronic heating. In Germany, there are DIN Standards for just about everything, and buddy, you had best meet those standards if you expect to do installations in Europe!

Some of the folks who were selling hydronic radiant tubing in America back then adopted DIN Standard 4726, which demands that hydronic systems not allow in any more than one-tenth of a milligram of oxygen, per liter of water, per day, when the water is 40 degrees Celsius (that's 104 degrees Fahrenheit for you New Yorkers). In case you're wondering, this is an extraordinarily small amount of oxygen. Nowadays, every tubing manufacturer has a product that will meet DIN4726, but that wasn't the case in the early Nineties, thus the controversy.

But having a tubing that meets DIN4726 isn't the only way you can protect a hydronic radiant system from oxygen-diffusion corrosion, and tubing manufacturers who weren't meeting the strict German standard were very vocal about this. You see DIN4726 doesn't demand that you do it a certain way; they just say DO IT! And you can do it in a couple of other ways.

First, you can separate the ferrous (iron and steel) parts of the system from the nonferrous parts of the system by using a stainless steel heat exchanger. The most popular are the braised-plate exchangers. Those are those tiny ones that look like silver bricks. They keep the water in the plastic or rubber tubing isolated from the steel and cast iron parts of the system, and they're perfectly acceptable.

You can also install a system that has no iron or steel in it, of course. Brass valves and circulators, copper boilers—these will do nicely because these materials won't rust.

Another way to prevent corrosion and meet the standard is to add corrosion-inhibiting chemicals to the system water. The trouble with chemicals, though, is that you have to monitor them from year to year because they lose their potency over time and can actually *cause* corrosion. In Europe, where everyone is very concerned about the environment and pollution, contractors avoid chemicals because there are few places to dump them when it's time to get rid of them. And that's why you find so much oxygen diffusion-barrier tubing in Europe. When those European tubing manufacturers began to market their goods in America, they didn't want contractors considering chemicals or heat exchangers as a viable option to what they were selling. I'm sure you can understand why.

Nowadays, literally every tubing manufacturer marketing in America sells a tubing that meets DIN4726. What's fun to watch, though, is how some of them are now encouraging American contractors to use heat exchangers or chemicals and *non*barrier tubing, which they offer at a lower price. Why would they do this? Because this tubing is less expensive! It gives them a better shot at the job.

So there you have it in a nutshell. Is oxygen-diffusion corrosion a real concern? Yes, but mainly on systems where the operating temperature is above 140 F. Should you protect every system you install by using either DIN-Standard tubing, a heat exchanger, or corrosion-inhibiting chemicals? Absolutely! Did some manufacturers make a bigger deal about this in the early Nineties than they had to? *I* sure think so.

As we grew smarter and gained experience, the oxygen-diffusion issue quietly went away. Knowledge is a very bright flashlight that shines into those dark rooms. Knowledge can help you see the flaws in an argument. You know *everything* you need to know, pal. It's all basic science and it's as close to you as that next bag of potato chips or that big red party balloon.

CHAPTER 8

. . . .

What's the Best Approach for *This* Job?

The neat thing about hydronic radiant heating is that you have loads of choices. There's really no one "right" way. You can get pretty creative with this stuff, and your imagination is about the only thing that limits what you can do. For instance, have you ever considered radiantly heating a kitchen countertop? If the folks are doing well enough to afford granite, I'll bet they'd be receptive if you tell them that their new countertop doesn't have to feel like a slab at the County Morgue.

Or how about attaching some hydronic tubing to the back of that cast iron bathtub so that when your customer leans back in that warm bath water, her heart won't stop beating when her warm shoulders hit that icy cast iron.

A buddy of mine put radiant tubing in the concrete that was to form an outdoor hot tub on the patio of a millionaire's new home. Now those rich folks can sit in their hot water and feel the warm stone and be perfectly content. Those folks *deserve* to be perfectly content, don't you think?

You can be as creative as you'd like. Let your imagination run wild. But first, you need to get the basics under your belt, so here's what you should know.

The basic idea is, well, pretty basic!

Your job is to get the radiant energy to flow toward the people. That won't happen until the floor, ceiling or walls warm up. And before you can make that happen, you have to move the heat out of the water and into the floor, ceiling or walls, and that happens not by radiation, but mainly by conduction. If you're putting the radiant tubing into a concrete floor, you have to transfer the heat from the water, through the wall of the tubing and into the floor. That's not difficult to do because the concrete surrounds the entire tube. If you're doing a staple-up job, it's tougher to move the heat into the floor by conduction because only a thin edge of the tubing touches the wood floor. This is why manufacturers sell heat-transfer plates. These plates (which I'll tell you more about later) hug more of the tubing and, since they're made of aluminum and have a lot of surface area spread across the floor, they quickly transfer the heat from the tubing into the wood floor.

Go back to the concrete floor for a moment. You want the heat to move upward toward the people, right? That's why it pays to put some insulation under the concrete slab. The more you insulate on one side, the more the heat will want to go the other way. Insulation is especially important along the edge of a concrete slab because the heat will easily move sideways toward the cold earth. This is how the folks in Levittown are able to grow their tulips in February. Insulating beneath the slab helps, but it's not as important as insulating around the perimeter because the earth under the slab doesn't change temperature as much as the earth next to the slab does. Think of the house as an insulating "blanket" that's keeping the little piece of earth beneath it warm.

If you staple the tubing to the underside of a wood floor, make sure you insulate below the tubing. But don't let the insulation come in contact with the tubing. Allow an air gap of about two inches, and use foil-faced, batt insulation with the foil facing upward toward the tubing. The shiny surface of the foil will help direct the rays of radiant energy that stream off the tubing upward toward the floor.

Next, consider the insulating value of the material between the tubing and the top of the finished surface. For instance, let's say you're putting the tubing into a concrete slab that's going to be covered with ceramic tile. Heat passes through concrete and ceramic tile pretty well. You'll keep that in mind when you're figuring out how much tubing you need, how far apart the rows should be, and the water temperature you'll need. But now let's say your customer wants to put a thick rug over that concrete floor instead of ceramic tile. The rug and the pad beneath the rug will behave like a heavy sweater on that floor. It will keep the heat from moving toward the people. You'll have to take this into consideration when you're sizing the job. And mention this to the people who will be living in the house because they just might decide to go from tile to rugs some day.

That's the basic idea – get the radiant energy to move in the direction of the people by using insulation to encourage it to go that way. Now let's take a look at a few different types of jobs.

Slab on Grade:

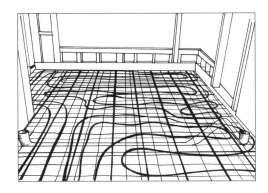

Here we have a slab of concrete that's sitting right on the ground. Generally, the tubing will be on 12-inch centers on these jobs. When you get near to a cold surface such as a window, you'll move the tubing closer together. As I mentioned earlier, I have a friend who does a lot of radiant work. He has a rule of thumb that works well for him. He'll measure the height of the cold exposure and then place his tubing on six-inch centers for a distance away from the exposure that's equal to one-third of its height. For instance, let's say there's a nine-foot-high wall of glass in a room he's trying to heat. He'll place tubing on six-inch centers for a distance of three feet in from the window. Then he'll do the rest of the room on 12-inch centers. In bathrooms, he always puts the tubing on six-inch centers because he knows that buck-naked people like warm rooms.

As I said before, it will be great if you can put insulation under the entire slab. If you can, use at least one-inch-thick polystyrene. The tongue-in-groove kind works best. Increase the thickness to two inches when you get within four feet of the edge of the slab. Remember, the heat wants to move toward the colder earth that's out there next to the house. The insulation will help corral the heat back toward the inside of the house and up toward the people.

All the way around the perimeter of the slab, you'll use polystyrene insulation, and this should be at least two inches thick. Extend the perimeter insulation down below the frost line; normally that would be about four feet.

Always use a vapor barrier under the slab. It can be polyethylene and it should be at least 6-mil thick. The vapor barrier does two things for you. First, it keeps the ground water from robbing the slab of its heat. Second, it won't let any water leak downward, should a tube break. Again, this was the trouble they had in Levittown years ago. They didn't use vapor barriers and when the copper began to leak, it leaked into the ground. No one knew this was happening because no water showed up on the floor. When you have a vapor barrier, the concrete will get wet because concrete is porous. Your customer will spot the leak and call you for help (what a great opportunity!).

As for the concrete slab itself, make sure you use reinforcing mesh. Lap the mesh over the edge of the slab by at least six inches. Check with the radiant tubing manufacturer as to the type of ties that they want you to use when you connect the tubing to the wire mesh. It pays to ask because there are some things you should not use. For instance, if you were to use duct tape to secure PEX tubing to the wire mesh, you would learn to your dismay that the glue in duct tape is not very nice to the chemical makeup of cross-linked polyethylene. Unfortunately, you will learn this after the concrete has hardened.

On most jobs, you'll set the tubing so that it's about two inches below the top of the concrete slab. It *will* work if you set it lower, but you'll have to run hotter water and controlling the temperature will be more difficult since you'll have to conduct the heat through more concrete before it can set itself free as radiant energy on the surface. I once visited a commercial building in Germany where the installer put the tubing six inches deep in the concrete. He did this because he knew the owner was going to drive anchors down into the concrete to stabilize his machinery. He used a slab sensor to control the surface temperature, and he never shut off the heat during the winter. The recovery time would have been ridiculous.

While pouring the concrete, you should always pressurize the tubing to at least 50-psi to keep it from collapsing and so you'll be able to spot any leaks. It's better to pressurize with air rather than water if you can because if there's a leak, air won't affect the composition of the concrete.

If you're using PEX tubing and you're pouring the concrete from a wheelbarrow, make sure you don't scratch the tubing with the front end of the wheelbarrow as you tip it up. It helps to put a piece of plywood under the end of the wheelbarrow until you get the hang of it. And always pour the concrete along the lines on which the tubes are running so the concrete can flow beneath them without causing the tubes to float up. Jiggle the wire mesh while you're pouring (get a helper to do this for you) so the concrete gets where it needs to go and the tubes don't sink too low. You can use a hook to do this if you want to save the wear and tear on your back, but if you do use a hook, make sure it has a blunt tip. You're laying radiant tubing here, not trying to haul a 400-pound tuna into a boat.

Once you get the concrete down, screed and trowel it as you normally would with any slab. As the concrete sets you'll have to lay in some control joints. Here's a photo of what they look like.

Control joints give the concrete a place to break as time goes by. All slabs need control joints because all slabs eventually break. That's why they put those lines in concrete sidewalks. Control joints divide a slab into smaller sections that can absorb the movement of the building. Avoid placing your tubing below a control joint, if you can. If you can't avoid it, put a sleeve over the tubing that's going to pass under the joint so that the concrete won't damage the tubing as it breaks over time.

Slab on top of framed floors

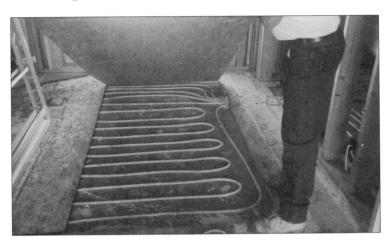

You can staple the tubing to the top of a frame floor and then pour concrete over it, but you first have to make sure the framing can handle the extra weight. This is really the call of the architect or engineer on the job, but you should make sure they're aware of what you're going to do. Hydronic radiant heating is new to a lot of architects and engineers and they often depend on the installer for advice. An inch and a half of concrete will add about 18 pounds per square foot to the load of the floor. That adds up! And if the architect doesn't think about it, the homeowners are going to wind up in the basement some day. An inch and a half of concrete will give you enough to cover your tubes, but again, make sure the architect considers this when he's figuring the height of the doors and the cabinets. It can't hurt to be too careful, right?

Insulate the space below the tubing to R-11 if the room below the floor is heated. Figure on R-19 if it's over an unheated basement, and R-30 if you're over a crawl space. The colder the space below, the greater the insulation should be. But you know that instinctively, right?

What do you do after the concrete dries? On this type of installation, probably install either ceramic tile or a rug right on top of it.

Slab with sleepers over a frame floor

Here's a photo of a Colorado job in progress. The "sleepers" aren't the guys who install the tubing (my friend Mark Eatherton, Colorado Madman, calls those guys "Tubesters"), they are the pieces of wood you see running back and forth across the floor. What's the wood doing there? It's there so the hardwood flooring guys don't hammer nails into the tubing. The tubing runs between those sleepers. It's stapled right to the top of the plywood floor, and in this picture, it's buried under a 1-$\frac{1}{2}$" layer of gypsum-concrete.

You don't have to use the gypsum-concrete, but I think you'll have a better job if you do because you'll have the benefit of that thermal mass. Below the floor there's insulation. That's to keep the heat from radiating down instead of up. There's also insulation at the ends of the joist bays to keep the heat from moving sideways and out through the walls of the house.

Notice how Mark Eatherton notches his sleepers to show where the tubing passes by.

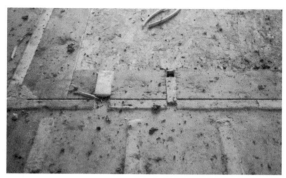

Mark has taught the hardwood guys that they had better not nail on an angle near those notches. If you ever met Mark Eatherton, you would listen to him *too*.

He has also instructed his Tubesters to do *this* on all of his jobs.

As the tubing circuits enter a room, they *always* pass directly over the center of the door frame. Everyone gets into the habit of knowing they're there and they don't hammer sharp things into the floor at that point.

Putting the tubing in a slab on top of a framed floor is a really common way of installing hydronic radiant heat in a house. And because it is, you should know something about this stuff most folks call GYP-CRETE because you'll probably be seeing plenty of it in the years to come.

The lighter side of concrete

Gypsum concrete is a mixture of very fine sand, gypsum, cement and bonding agents. It's been around since 1971 and if you use it instead of concrete your floors won't be as heavy. When it first came out, contractors used gypsum concrete for sound and fire control in multi-family construction, but when hydronic radiant floor heating reemerged, gypsum concrete seemed like a natural for that as well. Maxxon Corporation, 920 Hamel Road, Hamel, MN 55340 (1-800-356-7887) sells it under the registered trademark, GYP-CRETE-2000. A layer of GYP-CRETE that's ³/₄" thick weighs less than 6.5 Lbs/sq. ft. Normally, you'll pour it to a thickness of 1¹/₂", though. The folks from the company suggest you have the product applied in two separate three-quarter-inch applications, allowing the first coat to dry before applying the second. Friends who have used a lot of this stuff tell me this isn't necessary, though. They have it poured all at once and they've never had a callback.

GYP-CRETE levels itself as it gets poured on the floor from a hose. Make sure there are no holes in the floor when you're applying it because it will easily leak down to the floor below. Surprise!

Another company that makes a similar material is Hacker Industries, Inc., Box 5918, Newport Beach, CA 92662 (1-800-642-3455). They call their material Gyp-Span, and you should know about it because competition is *good*!

Gypsum concrete is lighter than concrete, but it can cost twice as much as concrete, especially if you're buying it in small quantities. Whether you choose Maxxon or Hacker, you can only get the material through a manufacturer-certified installer who then shows up with their own pumping truck. If the manufacturer-certified installer is far from you, expect to pay even more. For small jobs, you can buy a bag of the stuff from Maxxon (50 pounds) or Hacker (80 pounds). You just have to mix it with sand and water and pour it over the tubing.

You don't have to use gypsum concrete if you don't want to. You can substitute Portland-based cement mixed with a material called a superplasticizer and a couple of other agents. This material costs about one-third of what gypsum concrete costs.

My colleague at *Plumbing & Mechanical* magazine, John Siegenthaler, worked with a contractor friend, Harvey Youker, to come up with a lightweight concrete they call "The Youker Mix." Here's the recipe:

Batch material	Mix quantity
Type 1 Portland cement	517 pounds
Concrete sand	1,630 pounds
#1A (1/4" maximum) peastone	1,485 pounds
Air-entrainment agent	4.14 ounces
Hycol (a water-reducing agent)	15.5 ounces
Fiber mesh	1.5 pounds
Superplasticizer (WRDA-19)	51.7 ounces
Water	about 20 gallons

The recipe makes one cubic yard of 3,000-psi concrete floor topping (strength at 28 days). It's an easy-to-pour material that flows around the radiant tubing and conducts heat very well. John is one very smart and creative engineer who knows how to speak plain English, and you should check out his book, *Modern Hydronic Heating* (Delmar Publishers, 3 Columbia Circle, Albany, NY 12212-5105, ISBN 0-8273-6595-0). It's a good one.

Now that we've exhausted the upper side of the floor, let's take a look at what's possible from the *other* side.

Wood floor with tubing stapled below

You can staple the tubing under the floor if you want to instead of laying it on top in a bed of lightweight or gypsum concrete. This is a less expensive way to get the job done, but you have to be really careful when you plan a staple-up job. You won't have the thermal mass of concrete to work with because the tubing is under the wood floor, and there's no concrete involved.

Usually on a staple-up job you'll attach the tubing right to the bottom of the floor by placing a staple every six inches or so. The idea is to make the tubing touch the floor. Keep in mind that the heat transfer starts as conduction and becomes radiant only when it enters the room where the people are. The heat has to conduct through the walls of the tubing and enter the floor. The idea behind attaching the tubing to the floor is to make the tubing touch the floor so the heat can conduct into the wood. The trouble, though, is that only a thin edge of the tubing actually touches the floor. It's like the part of your car's tire that touches the road. When you put the tubing in a concrete slab, the entire surface of the tubing touches the floor because the concrete grabs the whole tube. This job costs less to install, but you have to run hotter water through it. There is *no* free lunch.

With this type of installation, you also have to bounce the radiant energy off the tubing and up onto the bottom of the subfloor so the top of the finished floor heats evenly all the way across. You'll use foil-faced insulation to do this. It's important to have the foil facing upward toward the floor, and it's crucial that you leave several inches of airspace between the tubing and the foil. That's so the radiant waves of energy can diffuse down within the joist bay and bounce back up onto the underside of the floor. A lot of installers make the mistake of pushing the insulation tightly up against the tubing when they do their first job. This seems to make sense at first; they figure if the insulation is packed in tightly, the heat won't leak out the bottom. But what actually happens is that the heat concentrates around the area where the tube touches the floor. Upstairs, the customer

can feel hot and cold spots on the topside of the floor. Had the
installer left the air gap between the foil and the tubing, the radiant energy would have had a place to bounce around and smooth
itself across the floor.

You can use clips to attach your batts of insulation to the bottom of the joist bays. That will give you a couple of inches of air
below the tubing and give you a floor with a relatively even surface temperature.

As I mentioned, some manufacturers sell aluminum plates
that help move the heat across the underside of the floor by conduction. Here's a product called RADIANT-TRAK™ that's
especially good for staple-up jobs.

You nail the plates to the underside of the floor and snap
the tubing right into the tracks. The aluminum grabs hold
of more of the tubing so the heat moves more quickly by
conduction. These add to the price of the job, of course,
but they also give you better control over the level of comfort upstairs. One thing you have to watch out for if you
use this product, though, is the outdoor temperature on the
day you install it. If the temperature drops down to zero
degrees F, or so, that night, the PEX just might decide to
drop out of the aluminum plates. This happens because
there's a difference between PEX and aluminum's coeffi-

cients of expansion. If you're expecting a frigid night, put a bead of silicone down the channel before you snap the tubing in place.

In the past few years, some tubing manufacturers have been recommending that you just hang the tubing in the joist bay and not attach it to the underside of the floor.

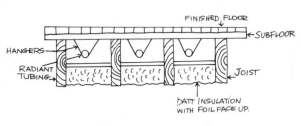

Here, you don't have the advantage of conduction since the tubing isn't touching the floor. The idea is to make the air trapped in the joist bay between the floor and the insulation hot. The heated air then warms the wood and the people upstairs get the radiant benefit. One installer told me he found this method to be very labor intensive since he had to lace the PEX tubing back and forth. It took longer than expected because he couldn't staple the tubing down anywhere. "It was whipping around like mad and driving us crazy," he said. "I'd never do it again." You also have to run higher-than-normal water temperatures with this method.

Something you have to keep in mind when you do any sort of under-the-floor installation is that if the job has old electrical wiring you have to get that wiring out of the joist bays before you make the air in those spaces hot. The ambient temperature old wiring can take isn't as high as what modern wiring can handle. You don't want to be blowing circuit breakers in that old house . . . or worse.

Lessons learned on one staple-up job

It was a mid-July day and the air was as still as swamp water. The shallow crawl space under Alan Levi's family room looked about as inviting as a pizza oven and we knew the fan we'd set up wouldn't help much. Not today.

"Well, what do you think?" Jake asked, pointing toward the narrow door under the porch. "Ready for the *real* world?" He smiled a knowing smile. I felt queasy.

Jake Greenwood is a master plumber. He works for OSI, the Long Island-based fuel oil dealer that my buddy, Alan Levi, Ace Troubleshooter, runs with his brothers. Jake's the kind of guy who will tackle just about any thing without complaining. Jake, Rick Taylor, another OSI installer, and I were going to spend the next few days installing a staple-up job in Alan's crawl space.

I had asked Alan to let me work with his guys on this installation because it was an unusually difficult one. I was trying to learn as much as possible about staple-up hydronic radiant heating, but I could get only so much from books and conversations. I needed a vicarious thrill and the opportunity to get my hands (and everything else) dirty, so I volunteered to make believe I was a tough guy for a day.

We were going to staple 900 feet of hydronic radiant heat tubing to the underside of the floorboards below Alan's family room. The tubing had to be roughly on eight-inch centers between the floor joists. I say "roughly" because we had to circumnavigate a few thousand nail tips that were sticking down a good $1/2$" from the underside of Alan's floor. We also had to work around electrical, alarm, stereo and telephone wires, plumbing pipes, and a very memorable wax toilet gasket. The crawl space, at best, was only 30 inches high and there were places where it dipped to about half that. In short, it was a perfect place to learn the hard way.

"Can we use a crawler in there?" I asked Jake.

"We can try," he said, looking at the rough concrete, "but I don't think it's going to roll very well." The concrete floor was about as smooth as a coral reef. In some places, it looked to be about as sharp.

"Put these on," Jake said, handing me a pair of worn leather kneepads. "You're gonna know you had those on after a couple of days," he said with a grin. He was right. The leather straps immediately began to cut into the back of my knees as I crawled into Alan Levi's hellhole.

Alan likes to try things out on himself before he sells the idea to a customer. Years ago when we were doing this job he had already installed a number of hydronic radiant heating systems in concrete slabs, and those always worked well, but he'd never tackled a staple-up job before. "It seems to me that if you're going to screw up, this is the place it'll happen," Alan told me. He'd heard a few stories about heating contractors who had signed on to do staple-up work and then ran into unexpected surprises. He wanted to get a sense of how much tubing his guys could install in a day, and how they felt about doing it, especially in tight crawl spaces.

And that's why I was in this horrible place on a murderously hot and humid day in July. "If we can do *this* one," Alan said, "we can do *anything*."

Alan chose to work with Heatway on this project. Heatway makes an extremely flexible, industrial strength hose that can handle the pressures and temperatures far beyond those you'll normally see in a hydronic system. The flexibility is what sold him in this case. He had used PEX in the past on slab jobs and found it to be an excellent material, but he thought the more flexible Heatway product would be best for the tight confines of his crawl space. He figured it would save us time.

Tim Ritter, one of Heatway's application engineers, took Alan's plans and sized the entire job. Tim used the company's software to do a radiant, heat-loss calculation, and then he laid out the hose size and spacing, the water temperature, the circulator, mixing valve and manifold sizing. He also told us how many feet of hose we'd need and provided us with a list of materials and a nomograph showing the effects different water temperatures and tube spacing would have on this particular room. Manufacturers can be *very* helpful.

The next thing we had to do was drill a series of holes through the floor joists from one end of the crawl space to the other. We used an angle drill to do this. It was a real buster working in that tight crawl space. Once we had the holes finished, we began to thread the hose through each in much the same way you would lace a sneaker. In theory, it sounds easy; in a tight crawl space, it's a nightmare. Trust me; it takes a *lot* longer than you think it's going to take.

You work off a pair of copper, brass, or plastic manifolds when you do hydronic radiant work. The manifolds we used on Alan's job were about a foot long and made of copper. Each had five, barbed connections. One of the manifolds came with five tiny balancing valves, which we used later on to adjust the flow through each circuit.

We had five rolls of hose to install. Four of the rolls were 200 feet long; the fifth was 100 feet long. That gave us a total of 900 feet for the project. We used an uncoiler to unravel the hose. I think it's good to limit the length of a circuit to 250 feet, if possible, because that keeps you within the range of "normal" circulators. You can run longer lengths if you need to but then you have to deal with higher pump heads and bigger temperature drops. To keep things simple on Alan's job, we restricted the maximum loop length to 200 feet, which made it more man-ageable in the crawl space.

I pulled each hose out to its full length in the street and then doubled it back onto the hose uncoiler, which looks like a Lazy Susan with a thick center post. When you double the hose back you mark its middle. Then you stick one end on a supply-man-ifold tapping, and the other on the return-manifold tapping. Next, you start lacing the "sneaker." We shoved the doubled-up middle of the hose through the holes in the joists, and then pulled portions of it down each joist bay. On Alan's job, we installed the manifolds in the boiler room, but we could have put them in the crawl space had we wanted to. This is a decision you make on each job. Whatever is easiest is usually the best. You'll supply one manifold with water from the boiler, and return the water to the boiler from the other manifold.

We stapled the hose to the underside of the floor as we went, and before long, we got into a rhythm where one of us would hold the tubing while Jake stapled. Heatway rented us the air-powered staple gun, which Jake found pretty easy to use—after he got used to it. He did manage to staple through the hose three times in the first hundred feet, but after that, he was flawless. You can fix Heatway's tubing in place with a repair kit—thank goodness! It's a lot easier on a workbench than it is in a crawl space, though.

You'll run into things on staple-up jobs that the manufacturers can't help you with. The instructions Tim Ritter gave us showed the joist holes in one location, but Tim had never been in this crawl space, and neither had we. What we learned the hard way was that the general contractors had used joist wood to make his cats. That presented us with three, solid-wood barriers that ran perpendicular across the crawl space— right in the way of where the tubing was supposed to go. We all moaned when we saw them. We didn't want to have to drill through all of the cats, so we improvised and rerouted the tubing as we went along.

We also ran into areas where the GC had doubled up on the joists. There was no room for the angle drill so we had to improvise once again with the tubing. There's no way in the world a salesman sitting upstairs at the kitchen table would have seen any of this.

And then there were the wires, the plumbing pipes, the nail heads, and that *very* memorable wax toilet gasket. We had to work around these challenges while scratching and sneezing and coughing from the fiberglass insulation that we'd taken down and laid to the side of the crawl space. The humidity soared to 90 percent. I felt like a galley slave and was more than ready to return to my word processor. None of this was in "the book," but now it's in *this* one, so be careful out there, pal.

Alan has cast iron, recessed radiators as well as copper fin-tube baseboard in the rest of his house. Those units call for 180-degree water on the coldest day of the year. His new radiant zone needed only 150-degree supply temperature so we used a three-way mixing valve to mix the water returning from the radiant zone with the hot water from the boiler. We put the return water into the "cold" port on the three-way valve. The "hot" port got the boiler water, and the valve blended the two to supply 150-degree water to the radiant zone's supply manifold through the "mixed" port.

Alan had been living with a loop of copper fin-tube baseboard in his family room, but it was never able to keep that bare hardwood floor warm. That's why we were doing this installation in the first place. He decided to leave the baseboard as a backup to the radiant system (should he ever need it). He set up the radiant system as a separate zone and installed a new thermostat for it, right next to the baseboard's thermostat. Then he set the radiant system's thermostat a few degrees higher than the baseboard's thermostat. We could have done the same thing with a two-stage thermostat, but we already had the one thermostat in place so he saved a few bucks.

Tim Ritter had designed Alan's floor temperature to be 83 degrees F, and that worked out as advertised. Only the most extreme winter temperatures caused the copper fin-tube baseboard zone to kick in, and those times were rare.

The thing to remember about staple-up, though, is that while some manufacturer's engineer can help you design it, that engineer is not going to get into that crawl space or basement with you. Nor can that engineer predict what you're going to find once you're down there. That's when you'll have to toss out the rule book and make some on-the-spot decisions – as you do every day.

And by the way, never install radiant heat tubing right next to a toilet's wax gasket. *Never*!

The Maurer Method

Speaking of throwing out the rule book, I once met a couple of guys from Colorado who did just that. Elwin and Bruce Maurer, father and son, do things differently on the eastern slope of the Colorado Rocky Mountains, and I'd like to tell you about them because they made me challenge my way of thinking. And whether or not you think they're wise, I hope they make you challenge the way *you* see the world of hydronics.

Most of the Maurer jobs have been of the staple-up variety. For years, they attached polybutylene tubing (which unfortunately is no longer available) to the underside of wooden subfloors, right between the joist bays—just like in Alan Levi's family room. "But we don't use staples," says Elwin. "We use electrical clamps instead, and we attach the clamps with screws. Clamps allow the tubing to move better than staples." This is an important consideration because plastic tubing expands quite a bit when you heat it. The Maurers buy more of these clamps (10,000 at a time) than any electrician in Colorado. "We probably buy more of these clamps than anyone else in the country," says Elwin. "We've tried other ways, but these clamps work the best."

The Maurers have attached miles of plastic tubing to the undersides of their customers' floors, and they've done it quickly. They pay one of their installers ten cents per foot to install the tubing between floor joists. He averages 3,000 installed feet of tubing in an eight-hour day, and his work is remarkably neat.

They use no gypsum or lightweight concrete, which Elwin and Bruce believe slows down the radiant floor's response time and can lead to comfort-related callbacks. "We also think that gypsum and concrete add considerably to both the cost of the job and the weight of the floor," notes Bruce. "By leaving it out, we're able to deliver radiant systems that fall within 15% of the cost of a typical copper fin-tube baseboard job."

Instead of boilers, they use high-efficiency, condensing water heaters. This is not a cost-savings measure, though, since these heaters usually cost as much as boilers. "We like them for their simplicity and reliability," says Elwin. They'll stage these condensing units to satisfy the radiant panels on both their residential and commercial work. By transferring heat through stainless steel, braised-plate exchangers, they're also able to make domestic hot water, using these same heaters.

The Maurers' goal is to design around a maximum supply water temperature of 140 degrees F. This involves paying close attention to the way the builder is insulating the house. "We always watch that," says Elwin. "Insulation can make or break a staple-up hydronic radiant job." Most of their jobs wind up with tubing on eight-inch centers in the joist bays.

For me, the most surprising aspect of a Maurer job is that Elwin and Bruce don't use compression tanks on any of their "staple-up" jobs. Instead, they've allowed the plastic tubing to take up the minimum expansion of the water as it heats to a maximum of 140 degrees F. "You can't do that if the tubing is encased in concrete, but it works fine when it's under the floor," says Elwin.

Their outdoor reset system is uncomplicated. It's also likely to raise your eyebrows if you've been following the growth of electronic controls since hydronic radiant heating became popular again. Instead of black-box technology, the Maurers opt for two, standard, normally closed zone valves piped on two boiler-bypass lines. They control these zone valves with two, simple, set-point controls, which sense outdoor air temperature on the north side of the building. When the outdoor temperature reaches, say, 45 degrees F, the first zone valve opens to bypass a portion of the water around the heater. As the day warms to 55 degrees F or so, the second zone valve will open to bypass more water around the heater and back to the floor. You wouldn't think something this simple could work, but it does.

For zoning, they use standard, air-temperature thermostats, which activate zone valves and stainless steel circulators. They have no concerns about oxygen-diffusion corrosion in their systems because, like their circulators, every component in their system is nonferrous.

To further reduce expenses, and to keep their jobs as simple as possible, they use just one manifold set, and it's always in the room with the water heater. All their circuits "home-run" to and from the boiler room, and most of their circuits average just over 300 feet in length.

The Maurers identify the tubing in each circuit by using masking tape of various colors. For instance, they might designate the living room's circuit by using three stripes, say, red, blue, and green. They ring the tape around both ends of the tubing to show which supply corresponds to which return. Each circuit has a different color code, along with a full-port ball valve, which they use to balance the circuit. Before they leave the job, they give the homeowner a chart showing what colors indicate which rooms. The homeowner is then free to adjust the flow of water to any circuit to satisfy the family's comfort needs. "The tape doesn't rub off like ink might," says Elwin. "It's simple, and it works." (Avoid using tape on PEX tubing, though. The chemicals in the glue don't get along well with PEX.)

See? There's more than one way to get the job done, and there's *plenty* of room for creativity.

Some things to consider when you're working with wood

If all you ever do is install hydronic radiant systems in concrete you will probably never go wrong because slab systems work almost in *spite* of you. I've seen contractors mess up by leaving out a good portion of the tubing, but the job worked anyway because of the thermal storage capability of concrete.

Wood's different. It doesn't hold heat well and, on staple-up jobs, only a portion of the hydronic radiant tubing touches the wood. You have to be especially careful with your design, and you have to be aware of what can happen to wood if you don't treat it properly.

The best type of wood for hydronic radiant floor heating is laminated softwood with a layer of hardwood on the top. This type of wood costs more than other types of wood flooring, but it delivers great results and it looks terrific. Manufacturers make this sort of flooring from thin plies of solid lumber, which they bond together. If you see a wood laminate that looks like it's solid wood, it's probably because the top layer is real wood veneer. It's great-looking stuff!

As with plywood, the grain of each layer of this sort of flooring is perpendicular to the layer directly above and below. By making it this way, the manufacturer can give the laminated wood flooring equal strength in all directions, which makes it stronger and less vulnerable to warping than solid-wood flooring. Manufacturers make both three- and five-ply laminated softwood. As you might expect, the five-ply product costs more. Because of the difference in ply, the thickness will vary from $5/16$" to $9/16$". Compare this to solid-wood flooring, which is typically $3/4$".

Laminated softwood is more easily damaged during construction and afterwards because of the thin veneer surface, however, and that's something you and your customer should consider. But it also doesn't expand and contract as much as nonlaminated solid wood flooring with changes in moisture content, and that's something you can put in the plus column. The more the wood expands and contracts, the better the chances are that it will crack. This is what makes nonlaminated or solid wood a lousy choice to sit over a hydronic radiant heating system. If the customer *insists* on solid-wood flooring, tell him to look for the type that's laminated in layers. Here again, you're mostly concerned with the wood's ability to go through countless cycles of expansion and contraction over the next 100 years or so. The homeowner might also consider what manufacturers call a "floating floor." This is tongue-in-grove wood that gets glued together and sits atop the subfloor as one piece when it's finished. It's not nailed to anything; it just sits there, held in place by its own weight – just like a rug. The installer will leave a gap around the entire perimeter for expansion and contraction, and then hide the gap with base molding. It's not a bad way to go.

Any wood product will expand and contract as its moisture content changes. Wood, after all, comes from trees. It used to be alive, and it's made of plant cells. When it expands and fills with moisture, some of the plant cells will get crushed. All it takes is a humid day. Then, when you turn on the new heating system, the wood will dry and contract. The cells that got crushed when the wood expanded will not bounce back very well. And this, my friend, is why wood floors crack. It doesn't take a hydronic radiant floor to do it, but when it happens, I'll bet they blame you. That's why you have to lay out the ground rules about wood floors *before* you take on the heating job. Wood flooring is bound to crack sooner or later. Your good efforts just speed up the process a bit.

Wood rules

I don't mean Wood *Rules*! When it comes to radiant, concrete is actually much better. I meant that there are certain *rules* you had better observe when you're working with a hydronic radiant system that involves wood. Ignore them and your life might get a tad too interesting.

1. The wider the boards, the greater the chance for trouble. Try to stick with boards that are no wider than three inches. Wide wood will probably warp.

2. Sell mechanical humidity control. Ideally, the relative humidity in a hydronic radiantly heated home that has wood floors should be no more than 50 percent. "Without this constant humidity, you must live with the cracks," according to the experts at the National Oak Flooring Manufacturers Association.

3. Realize that the seeds of the damage will be planted during construction. That's because this is when the concrete in the building is wet. As the concrete dries, the moisture leaves it and heads toward the wood. Tape a square of clear, plastic sheeting over the concrete and watch it for moisture. Don't let the carpenters install the wood flooring over your new system until the plastic proves there's no moisture left in the concrete.

4. Provide heat and ventilation during construction. You have to do this because the painters and plasterers are adding gallons of moisture to the indoor environment. If you don't get rid of it, all that water is going to wind up in the wood floor. The damage won't show up until you turn on the system. And by that time, the other guys will be long gone.

5. Summertime means more humidity. So after that first summer when your new system kicks in, the wood might crack. It's not your fault, but rest assured, you will be blamed unless you make things clear to the homeowner before you begin.

6. Become the proud owner of a moisture detector. Spend a hundred bucks or so and get your own. It's a great tool to have if you're going to stay in this business. Keep a log of the finish wood's moisture content as the job progresses. You're aiming for 6% moisture, tops, before you turn on the heating system under that new floor.

7. Run the heating system for about five days before you let the carpenters install the finish wood. This will help dry out the wood. I remember visiting a famous movie actor's home in Park City, Utah while it was still under construction. The finish wood sat on a skid in the corner as the radiant floor ran wild and uncontrolled in the subfloor's gypsum concrete. It must have been 90 degrees F in that house and they hadn't even installed all of the windows yet! This was in late October, by the way. That wood was pretty dry before they nailed it in place! If you can't run the heat beforehand, lay down an 8-mil polyethylene vapor barrier between the concrete or gypsum concrete and the wood. That should keep the wood from sucking up the water.

8. Avoid using any paper containing tar or horsehair under the wood floor. These things can stink to high heaven when the heat comes on. And the stench stays with you for a long, long time. Use red resin paper instead, and if you're doing a retrofit, staple-up job, drill up through the floor to check for that ominous tarpaper or horsehair.

9. Never make a wood floor hotter than 85 degrees F at its surface. Even if the homeowner is planning on rugs. It's not good for the wood. Consider using a setpoint control to monitor the wood's surface temperature instead of an air-temperature thermostat. You may have to have some sort of supplemental heat in the room if an 85-degree surface won't get the job done on those really cold days. Whether or not you'll need this depends, of course, on the room's heat loss and the size of the floor.

10. Educate your customer about the small gaps that may appear in the floor. This happens when there's a urethane finish on the floor and the floor is made from nonlaminated solid wood. The finish actually "glues" the individual boards together, and as the wood expands and then contracts, the contraction will localize itself and wind up as a gap. This is so common with hardwood floors (whether they have hydronic radiant heat under them or not) that the hard wood flooring industry even has a name for it. They call the phenomenon, "panelization." Tell your customer about it *before* you start the job. Show them this book. (Hey Mr. Homeowner! It's not your heating contractor's fault!)

If you have questions about wood floors, you can get more information by contacting these folks. They provide brochures that say pretty much the same things I'm telling you. Get some of those brochures and include them with your proposals. The warnings sound so much friendlier when they're not coming from you.

National Oak Flooring
Manufacturers' Association, Inc.
PO Box 3009
Memphis, TN 38173-0009
Telephone: (901) 526-5016

The Hardwood Council
PO Box 525
Oakmont, PA 15139
Telephone: (412) 281-4980

C H A P T E R 9

. . . .

To the Boiler Room!

Let's put one of these hydronic radiant systems together. Since this is a practical guide for nonengineer installers and not some fancy book for engineers, I'm going to keep things simple. I want to give you loads of options so you'll be able to meet the needs of just about any customer you meet, but I also want to keep those options as simple as they can be. There's nothing here you don't already know. You just might not know that you know it.

Sound good? Okay, let's do it.

A lot of what I'm going to talk about here comes from a little book I wrote a few years ago called *Pumping Away*. There wasn't much original thought in that book; I borrowed a lot from people who are far brighter than I am. One of the guys I borrowed from was Gil Carlson, who is currently a Dead Man, but who was once Bell & Gossett's Director of Technical Services. He popularized this concept of pumping away from the compression tank and made a big name for himself among the engineering community. I repeated (in simpler terms) what he said and loads of contractors gave it a try. They found that when they piped a boiler room in a particular way they wouldn't have to go upstairs and bleed the radiators. They also found their systems were quieter and their customers were happier. Everybody won.

The business about the circulator and the compression tank went like this:

1. A closed hydronic system has just so much water in it.

2. You put air in the compression tank so that when you heat the water, and said water expands, it will have a place to go (and something to squeeze).

3. The circulator doesn't lift the water to the top of the system because there's already water up there. The fill valve saw to that. The circulator in a closed hydronic system is sort of like the motor on a Ferris wheel. It doesn't do any lifting; it just "turns" the water. And as with a Ferris wheel, the weight going up gets balanced by the weight coming down. There is no lifting. Just turning.

4. As the water flows through the piping, *none* of it can enter the compression tank because there's just so much water inside the system. Think about it. If the water left the pipe to go into the compression tank, there would be nothing to take the place of the "missing" water. In other words, you would be left with outer space in your pipe, and this, of course, is impossible. So I can tell you with *great* certainty that a circulator in a closed hydronic system cannot add water to the compression tank.

5. As the circulator moves water by the compression tank's connection, it can't suck any water from the tank into the pipes because the pipes are already filled with water, and water is *not* compressible. You can't get ten pounds in a five-pound bag. So I can tell you with *great* certainty that a circulator in a closed hydronic heating system cannot remove any water from the compression tank.

6. Since the circulator can neither add nor remove any water from the compression tank, the circulator cannot affect the

pressure inside the compression tank because it can't compress or decompress the air. The only thing that can change the pressure inside the tank is the expansion of the water when it gets heated or the contraction of the water when it cools.

7. This means that as far as the circulator is concerned, the compression tank becomes a "point of no pressure change," which is the term Gil Carlson, Dead Man, coined.

8. Now pay attention because this is the most important part. A circulator in a closed hydronic system isn't really a "pump." It doesn't actually produce pressure; it produces a *difference* in pressure. That's a very subtle thing that may be hard to get through your thick skull, but for now, please take my word for it. The important thing is that a circulator can move water just as easily by *dropping* the pressure on its suction side as it can by *increasing* the pressure on its discharge side. You still okay? Good.

9. Now, since the compression tank is the "point of no pressure change," the circulator will use it as a reference point. If you pump *away* from the compression tank, the circulator will show its differential pressure as an *increase* in pressure within the system. If you pump *toward* the compression tank, the circulator will show its differential pressure as a *decrease* in pressure on the system. Got it? Great! Read on.

10. Since air dissolves in water in *direct* proportion to the system pressure, when you *increase* the system pressure (by Pumping Away) it will be very easy to get rid of system air. However, if you insist on putting the circulator on the return side of the boiler, pumping *toward* the compression tank, the resulting *decrease* in system pressure will release the air that's dissolved in the water. That will have you bleeding radiators until you're as old as your Grandpa. And you know what, pal? That's probably very appropriate since *he's* the guy who told you to put the circulator on the return in the first place.

11. So there!

12. Now go read *Pumping Away* if you'd like the full tour.

The Pumping Away Module

This will save you time and money on every job you do from now on. The idea is to set up your boiler room so that you can easily get at everything when it's time for service. That means you should try to get all the important stuff between service valves. Here's a drawing of a basic Pumping Away module.

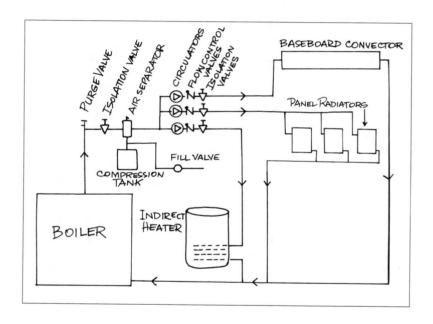

Come up out of the boiler into a tee with a boiler drain. The boiler drain will be your purge valve for the whole system when you're first starting up. Right after the boiler drain tee you have a main shutoff valve. This can be either a gate valve or a full-port ball valve. The next component should be a really good air separator, one that can catch microbubbles. Here's a picture of the first of these wonderful devices to come on the scene a few years back. It's called a Spirovent. I *love* this thing.

The older generation of air separators worked by getting the water to flow in what engineers call a "laminar" way. Laminar is the opposite of turbulent. When the water is laminar, the air bubbles will rise to the top of the pipe. The older generation of air separators "scooped" the air out of the flow by using a baffle that directed the larger air bubbles into a low-velocity chamber within the device. From there, the bubbles went either up into

the steel compression tank, or they left the system through an automatic air vent.

New air separators, such as the Spirovent, don't depend on laminar flow. They work by a process called "collision and adhesion." Simply put, they put a metal mesh in front of the flowing water. The tiniest air bubbles collide with the metal and cling to it by surface tension. It's beautifully simple and I know you've seen the principle many times. Let a glass of tap water sit on a table overnight. Notice those bubbles stuck to the inside of the glass in the morning? That's surface tension.

These new air separators are the neatest things to come down the pike in a long, long time, and you should not be without them on your jobs. Do they cost more? You bet! But they're *worth* it. Just add the cost into your price. You will be happier, and so will your customers. Trust me on this, if you haven't already learned the lesson on your own.

Your compression tank hangs from the bottom of the air separator, and your system fill valve goes in the space between the air separator and the compression tank.

Here's a picture of a fill valve.

Figure out how much water pressure you need to lift water to the highest point in the system. One-psi water pressure will lift water 2.3 feet straight up, no matter what size the pipe is. Once you've figured out what you need to fill the system, add three-psi pressure to that so you'll have some pressure at the highest point. You'll need that high-point pressure to get rid of the air. Once you get the system pressure set, close the fill valve. These things have no business remaining open. If a well-built, closed system needs additional water that means there's a leak somewhere. Your job is to find it. Protect your hydronic systems with low-water cutoffs, not feed valves.

Check the air pressure inside the compression tank (if you're using a tank with a diaphragm). The air pressure should equal the pressure you plan to use on the waterside of the diaphragm.

Check the air pressure *before* installing the tank and filling the system with water. If you wait until there's water inside the tank you won't be able to get an accurate reading on the airside of the diaphragm.

Next come the circulators.

In my diagram, I'm showing three of them – one serves an indirect water heater, the second is for some panel radiators, and the third is for a baseboard loop. Each circulator has a flow-control valve to prevent gravity circulation in the zone when the circulator is off.

A flow-control valve doesn't actually "control the flow," even though the name implies it does. All a flow-control valve does is prevent the hot

water from rising into the piping when the zone circulator is off. Inside a flow-control valve you will find a weighted check. That's all. The knob on top of the flow-control valve is there to crank the weighted check off its seat, should you ever want to bypass the flow-control feature.

And then we have a service valve after each flow-control valve. This can be either a full-port ball valve or a gate valve. Don't use globe valves in your hydronic systems because they offer too much resistance to flow and add to the size of the circulator you'll need for the zone. When it's time to service any of the components, all you have to do is close the shutoff valve upstream of the air separator, and the shutoff valves downstream of the flow-control valves.

When you're first filling this system, you close the main shutoff valve and open the boiler drain on that first supply-pipe tee to purge the air.

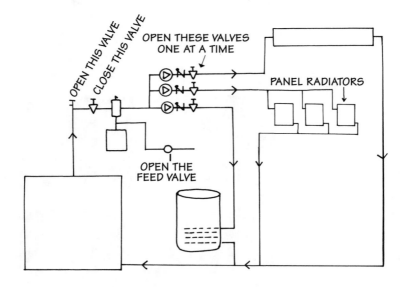

Then you use the fill valve to blow the air from one zone at a time. The water flows first through the system and then into the bottom of the boiler. There's no place for air to hide when you pipe a boiler room this way.

Once you do your initial fill and start the boiler, more air will come out of the cold water. Since you're Pumping Away, the circulator will add pressure to the water to keep the air from separating from the water. The air stays in solution until the microbubble air separator can catch it.

None of this is original. I've just used ideas developed by people who are far smarter than I am. The concept of Pumping Away has saved thousands of installers countless hours of bleeding radiators, and if you haven't tried it yet, you are going to be pleasantly surprised when you do.

Other things you may want to include in your Pumping Away module

Zone valves: Instead of using a bunch of circulators, you might want to have one circulator feeding several zone valves. Again, notice how you have just about everything that will ever need service between those service valves.

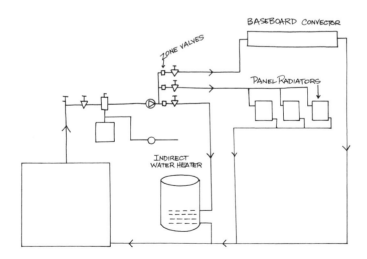

When one of the zones calls, the zone valve opens and trips an end switch that starts the circulator. The circulator runs until the thermostat or aquastat (in the indirect water heater) is satisfied. Then the valve shuts, turning off the circulator just before it closes.

Let me give you a tip that I learned the hard way about a certain zone valve. Honeywell makes a popular zone valve that sometimes creates water hammer if you use it in a Pumping Away system.

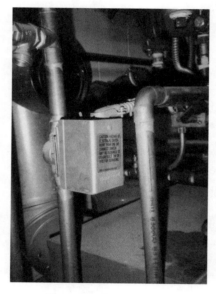

The hammering happens when one zone valve tries to close while another zone valve is still calling for heat. Since the closing zone valve can't shut off the circulator (the other zone keeps it on), the valve is fighting the flowing water. When the valve finally shuts, it often does it with a BANG! The Honeywell valves work best in a Pumping Away system if you pipe them on the *return* manifold rather than on the supply side.

Differential pressure regulator When you use any sort of zone valves you have to size your circulator to provide the water the system will need when all the zone valves are wide open. But suppose you have five zone valves and just one of them opens? What happens to the rest of that water? How does the circulator know what to do?

The answer lies in the way circulators perform. They run on a curve that balances the flow against the *resistance* to flow. Centrifugal pump manufacturers publish these charts they call "pump curves" that show the relationship between flow and resistance to flow. Here's what one looks like.

The line across the bottom represents the flow rate in gallons per minute. The line on the left represents the resistance to flow. The circulator's ability to overcome resistance to flow is called pump "head." In any closed hydronic system, the circulator will find a place where it will move as much water as it can against the resistance it "feels" in the system at any given time. The amount of water it can move changes as zone valves open and close. The more open valves there are, the more water the circulator will move. But you know that already, don't you?

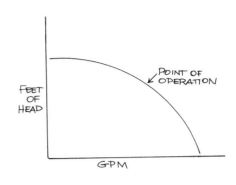

Anyway, if only one of those five zone valves opens, just so much water is going to fit through the valve. Water's not compressible, is it? You can get just so much through that "open door." The circulator tries to shove all it can through the opening, but the pipe can't take it so resistance builds and the circulator backs up on its curve. It looks like this.

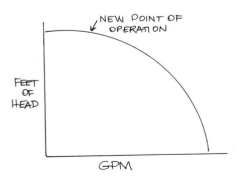

You see what the resistance to flow has done? It's pushed the circulator back so that it's now moving less water. But look at how the Pump Head has increased. The pressure has built up because the circulator is just as strong as it was before, but now it has all this pent-up energy. And that's where a differential-pressure regulator comes in. With all that pent-up energy, the circulator is liable to move the water through that single, open zone so quickly that it will create velocity noise. Velocity noise sounds like a whine or a hum and it's guaranteed to get your customer's attention. The differential-pressure regulator senses the build-up in pressure and opens to give the excess water a place to go. Here's what one looks like.

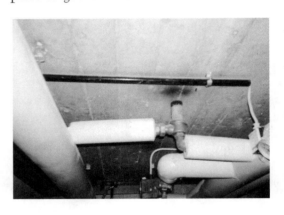

It goes between the circulator's discharge and the return side of your Pumping Away module. It has the effect of nailing the circulator to one point on its pump curve, and it does a mighty fine job of eliminating velocity noise. In Germany, where just about every house has thermostatic radiator valves, you'll find a differential-pressure regulator in just about every boiler room. *Very* good stuff!

Low-water cutoffs: Only a few states require low-water cutoffs on hot water boilers that aren't in commercial buildings or multifamily housing. Nevertheless, I believe *every* hot water boiler needs a low-water cutoff. This is especially true for hot water boilers that serve radiant systems because the tubing is usually below the boiler and often buried in concrete.

Should a buried tube spring a leak you'll be depending on the feed valve to make up the missing water. The feed valve can feed for a long, long time before anyone notices that something's wrong. And in the time it takes to notice, loads of fresh water with many pounds of lime can enter that boiler. The lime can block the movement of the water through the boiler and cause the boiler to dry-fire and break in no time at all. And yes, a dry-firing boiler *can* burn down the house. Which is why I think every boiler needs low-water protection. Low-water cutoffs save lives. The cost of the thing disappears in the price of the job, and if you're smart, you'll start using them on *every* job. Just screw it into a tee on the supply manifold, above the top of the boiler, and you'll be doing your customer a real service.

And the angels in heaven will smile down upon you.

Multiple boilers: Two boilers are better than one because it doesn't get that cold every day. I think it makes sense to use as many as four boilers on a job. You just divide the design-day (coldest day of the year) load among the boilers and pipe them like this.

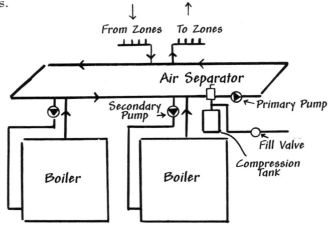

The piping I'm showing you here is called primary/secondary. It's a way of making sure no water flows through a boiler that's off. By keeping the water out of the "off" boiler, you save your customer money because you cut down on stand-by losses (that's the heat that would otherwise be going up the chimney). Here's what you ought to know about primary/secondary pumping.

Primary/secondary pumping: Gil Carlson, whom I mentioned before, wrote technical books for engineers, he invented and patented new products, and he traveled the country lecturing to groups of engineers about things hydronic. He was a legend in his own time, and he also helped contractors troubleshoot big projects in the early days of hydronic heating.

Back in the 1950s when hot water heating was still pretty new in big buildings, an engineer designed, and a contractor installed, a Monoflo® system in a big building. The engineer laid out the job so that it had a vertical loop of piping that went from the basement to the top floor. On each floor, he figured there would be a perimeter loop of radiation. He took each loop off the vertical main, using Blue Ring Monoflo fittings. B&G doesn't make these Blue Ring fittings any more. They still make fittings they call Red Ring, however. The Blue Ring fittings created a really severe pressure drop along the main and diverted lots of water into the branch circuits.

You see, that's the way a Monoflo system works. The water flows through a single pipe, and some of it gets sent toward the radiators because of these Monoflo tees. They have restrictions inside them that make it tougher for the water to go straight, so some of it goes out through the bull (the side) of the Monoflo tee. The return tee is in the same pipe as the supply tee, and that's why they call this a **Mono**flo system. Here's what one looks like.

Anyway, as I was saying, the engineer designed that old system and the contractor installed it just as the engineer said he should, but it didn't work. Oh, the main got hot all right! That wasn't the trouble. The trouble was that the radiators were stone cold. No water flowed that way. The engineer didn't know what to do so he got together with the contractor and together they asked the folks at Bell & Gossett for some help. B&G sent Gil Carlson.

Well, Gil got to the job and took a look around. He figured, correctly, that the water was finding it easier to flow along the main than it was to flow through the branches of those Monoflo tees and out toward those long perimeter loops. In his inventor's mind, Gil must have seen the struggle that water was having. He must have realized it needed a little help. So he told the engineer and the contractor to install a booster circulator on each perimeter loop. He figured that would change the balance of power and encourage the water to flow around the perimeter loops instead of straight through those Monoflo tees. He told the engineer and the contractor to keep the main circulator in the basement running. The booster circulators would just act as helpers.

They did as he suggested and the job worked just fine.

When Gil Carlson got back to Bell & Gossett's offices in Morton Grove, Illinois, just outside of Chicago, someone asked how he had made out on that job he visited. He told the story and they all began to talk about the possibilities. Suppose, for instance, they were to leave the main circulator on. They called that one the "primary" circulator because it had been there first. Then they could start and stop the booster circulators (they called these the "secondary" circulators because, even though they were important, they had come, well, second!) They could zone with those secondary circulators, and that would give them greater control over the system. Instead of operating hand valves at the radiators, they could put a thermostat somewhere in the middle of each floor and control the entire floor by starting and stopping the secondary circulators. That would be great, wouldn't it?

The next thing they asked themselves was whether they even needed those Monoflo tees now that they had the secondary circulators. If the water didn't want to flow through to the radiators with the Monoflo tees in place, it would be even *less* likely to go that way if they used standard, run-of-the-mill tees. Unless they started a secondary circulator, that is. And wouldn't that be even better?

So that's what they did. They set up some experiments where they used regular tees off a primary main. They ran the primary circulator all the time and they started and stopped the secondary circulators. Their simple system looked like this.

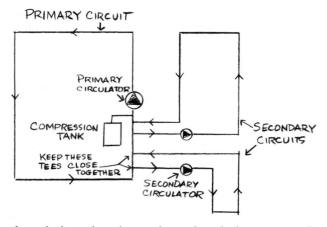

They found that the closer they placed those tees, the less likely water would be to stray off of the primary route when the secondary circulator was idle. They came up with a rule of thumb that said those tees should be pretty close together, never more than a foot apart. Sure, you could put them further away from each other if you wanted, but the further you moved them, the more stray flow you would get into the secondary circuit. So why not just keep them close together in the interest of better control?

And that's how primary/secondary pumping came to be. The rest, as they say, is history.

In a hydronic radiant system, you can use primary/secondary pumping in lots of ways. One way is to protect the boiler from low-temperature return water. Here, check this out.

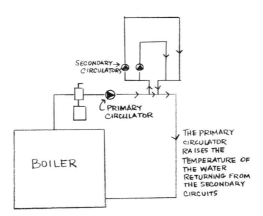

Do you see how the primary circulator is taking water out of the boiler and making it available to the secondary circuit? The primary circulator will run only if the secondary circulator starts. The two always run together, and the primary's job is to make hot water available to the secondary. The secondary circulator usually removes only a portion of what the primary supplies. The rest of the primary flow continues on and mixes with the water that's returning from the secondary circuit. The result is that the water that flows back into the boiler is hotter than it would be if just the secondary flow returned by itself. This lessens the chance that flue gases will condense inside the boiler, and it's one reason why so many boiler manufacturers love primary/secondary pumping. It's especially important in a radiant system, as you will see.

Here's another good thing about primary/secondary pumping. If you have a copper-fin-tube boiler, the flow rate moving across the boiler's heat exchanger is critically important. If the water moves too slowly it will flash to steam and create a racket. Primary/secondary pumping ensures that the right flow will always move through the boiler. Copper-fin-tube boiler manufacturers *really* love primary/secondary pumping.

If you have more than one boiler you can use primary/secondary pumping to make sure no water flows through a boiler that's not operating. Here, look.

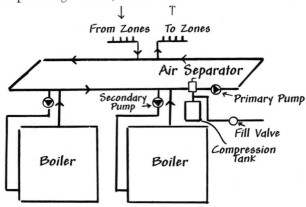

Two boilers are better than one because chances are slim that both will stop working on the same day. Besides, it doesn't get that cold every day, and if you size one boiler for the entire load, it will short-cycle and run inefficiently most of the year when the temperature is mild. If you split the total required load into parts, you can use multiple boilers and let one (or more) rest on days when it's not that cold outside. By piping the boilers this way, you can make sure that the water flows only through boilers that are firing. That saves energy because it reduces the "off" boiler's stand-by losses. It also lengthens the firing cycle of the "on" boilers and gives them better combustion efficiency.

When you're doing any sort of primary/secondary pumping you should use flow-control valves on the secondary circuits to keep hot water from moving by gravity into a circuit when its circulator is off. Since gravity circulation can happen on either end of the secondary circuit, you might consider using *two* flow-control valves for each circuit one on the supply and the other on the return. And make sure the arrows on the flow-control valves face in the right direction. If I were you, I'd put one on the supply side to start. You can always add a second on the return side, should you need it (which you may not).

It also helps with the initial air purge if you put a full-port ball valve in the primary circuit between the two secondary tees. This lets you force water up through the secondary. Once you've filled the system, you won't use these ball valves again. They're strictly for purging. Here's a sketch of what I mean.

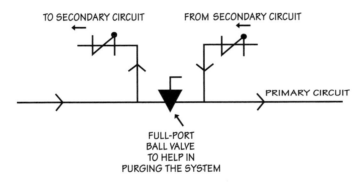

TO SECONDARY CIRCUIT   FROM SECONDARY CIRCUIT

PRIMARY CIRCUIT

FULL-PORT
BALL VALVE
TO HELP IN
PURGING THE SYSTEM

Bypass lines: When you're working with radiant you're working with relatively cool water. The trouble with this is that most boilers like *hot* water. In fact, if you bring water back to a cast iron boiler that's cooler than 140 degrees F, you're liable to damage the boiler. It's very easy to do this when the water flowing *out* to your radiant zone is typically only about 120 degrees F. That water is probably coming back at about 100 degrees F.

But there's an easy way around this. We already looked at primary/secondary pumping, which will protect the boiler *every* time, but there's a simpler, but cruder, way to get the job done. It's called a bypass line. Its job is to take some of the hot water that's leaving the boiler and blend it with the water that's coming back from the system. It's just like adjusting the water in a shower. You mix a bit of hot with a bit of cold to get "just right."

Most boiler manufacturers include simple drawings of bypass piping arrangements with their installation-and-operating instruction booklets. They usually show two types of bypasses and you have to make sure you don't get these confused because they can really mess you up. Watch.

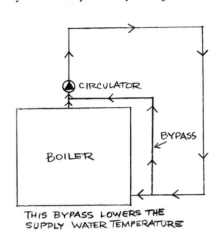

THIS BYPASS LOWERS THE SUPPLY WATER TEMPERATURE

In this drawing the bypass line goes from the return side of the system to the suction side of the circulator. Some of the returning water will come up from the return and mix with the hot boiler water. This will lower the temperature of the water flowing out to the system. It's a crude way to lower your supply temperature if you're trying to temper the water for a radiant zone, and this is how the Dead Men once did radiant, but this bypass doesn't protect your boiler (as they often found out to their dismay).

This is more like it.

Here, you're blending hot boiler water back into the return to raise the temperature of the stuff coming back from the system. This is the right way to do it with radiant. And by the way, if you have more than one cir-

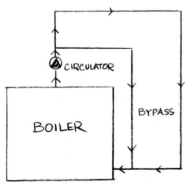

THIS BYPASS RAISES THE RETURN WATER TEMPERATURE

culator, you'll need more than one bypass line. If you're zoning with circulators, each one needs its own bypass. This is one of those nasty little bypass facts of life that make primary/secondary pumping so attractive to installers.

Using a bypass line will protect a boiler against low-temperature return water, but it's not very automatic. There *is* a better way. Here, read on.

Thermostatic bypass valves: This is a *much* better way to handle a small system because it's fully automatic. A thermostatic bypass valve protects the boiler against low-temperature water. Danfoss Automatic Controls offers the Esbe valve and I find this one to be beautifully simple. It has three, clearly labeled ports and contains a thermostat that's similar to the one in your car's radiator. The thermostat keeps the boiler water circulating around the boiler until the water reaches a certain minimum temperature. Then the thermostat lets it out into the system. You can use the valve in two ways.

If you put it on the boiler's supply line, the valve will let the water out into the system as soon as the boiler heats it up to 160 degrees F. At any temperature below 160, the water just flows around and around the boiler

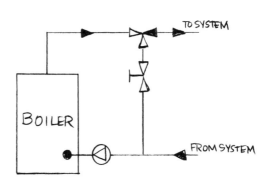

loop. Between 160 and 170 degrees F, the valve bypasses some of the hot boiler water back into the return side to raise the temperature of the water that's coming back from the system. As soon as the boiler reaches 180 degrees F, all the water flows into the system.

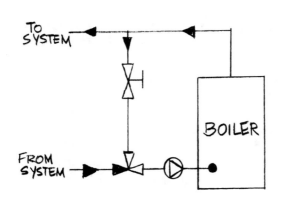

If you put the Esbe valve on the return side of the boiler it works a bit differently. Here, it will bypass most of the boiler water until the water returning from the system reaches 140 degrees F, which is the minimum safe temperature for most cast iron boilers. When the return temperature gets up to about 160 degrees F, the valve lets all the boiler water out into the system. Not too shabby, eh?

Indirect water heater: An indirect water heater is a tank that holds domestic hot water for you. It has no fire inside of it. Instead, it uses hot water from the boiler as a heat source. The boiler treats the indirect water heater as if it were a zone. There are a few kinds of indirect water heaters. Some have the boiler water inside a coil and the domestic hot water inside the tank. Others reverse this by putting the domestic hot water in the coils and allowing the boiler water to flow through the tank. They all look pretty much the same, these indirect water heaters, very much like their direct-fired brethren, but minus the burners. In fact, the one I have in my house once confused the building inspector. We had added a dormer to our Cape Cod home and we put the indirect water heater in a closet on the second floor. You can do that with an indirect water heater. The inspector started to write us up, saying we couldn't have a water heater on the second floor of the house. I tried to explain that it wasn't a water "heater." It was really just a storage tank. "You can't have it!" he insisted. When I pressed him for a reason he said, "You can't have a fire on the second floor." I asked him if he would show me the burner and he dutifully looked around for it. "It's probably electric," he said. "It has to go."

"Where's the heater cable?" I asked.

He pointed at the aquastat wire. "There," he grumped.

"Gosh, I don't know. You think that wire's heavy enough to carry the power necessary to heat all this water?" I hugged the heater and smiled at him.

"It goes!" he sputtered.

I had to appeal to a higher court, but that indirect heater remains in my daughter Meghan's closet – on the second floor.

Here's a picture of one that has the domestic hot water in the tank.

If you had a Pumping Away module and you were taking advantage of primary/secondary pumping techniques, you might pipe your indirect water heater this way.

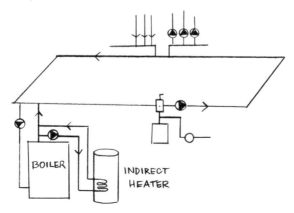

Here we have the heater as a secondary zone off the boiler. The boiler itself is a secondary circuit within this system. It provides hot water as needed to the primary circuit that's continuously directing water around the building during the winter. When the indirect heater needs a boost, the boiler circulator and the indirect water heater's circulator both start, as does the burner. I've piped it this way because it gives you a way of providing the indirect heater with boiler water during the summer when the building doesn't need any heat. During the summer, the same two circulators will run, but instead of the hot water flowing into the primary heating main, it will just circle back into the boiler. The indirect takes what it needs from the passing flow. It's very simple and it works!

The other type of indirect heater that I mentioned has the boiler water inside the tank and the domestic water in the tubes. You can use this type of heater to add water volume to your secondary boiler loop, if you'd like.

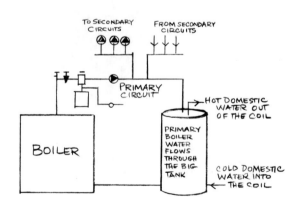

You see what I'm doing here? I've put the heater right in the boiler's loop. That adds volume to the boiler and allows the burner to run longer and more efficiently. This is a good way to overcome the short cycling that often causes concern when you use a low-water-content boiler. The indirect tank I'm using here is called an Ergomax™. I think this is one of the most useful hydronic "tools" around, and I'm about to tell you why.

Tempering tank: As I said, if you decide to use a small, low-water-content boiler you might have some concerns about short cycling. Little boilers come on and go off a lot more frequently than high-water-content boilers. One way around this is to use a tempering tank. A tempering tank acts as sort of a "wide space in the road" that contains a lot of water. It gives the little boiler something to work against so it can stay on longer and be more efficient. It also gives you closer control over the temperature of the water flowing out to your radiant panels because the tempering tank takes longer to heat (and cool) and remains more stable, as far as temperature goes. Simply put, a tempering tank is a big wet heat sink.

You can use an Ergomax indirect water heater as a tempering tank, which is why I like it so much. You can get your domestic hot water from the Ergomax and keep your little boiler from short cycling.

Here's a Pumping Away module with a primary/secondary set up. The Ergomax tank is in the boiler's circuit. Whenever water flows out of the boiler it has to pass through the Ergomax tank before it can return to the boiler. This gives you longer firing cycles and better combustion efficiency. Your heating circuits come right off the boiler's circuit, and the domestic hot water comes out of the Ergomax. You need a domestic hot water mixing valve

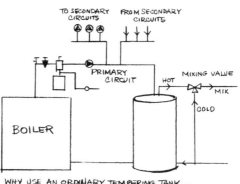

when you use the Ergomax as a tempering tank, but that's a small price to pay for all that you get in return. During the summer, you continue to get all the domestic hot water you need without having to heat the building. Not bad, eh?

Alternative heat sources: Since radiant panels run on such low-temperature water you can make the water warm with things other than boilers. Many installers are using water heaters, for instance. These are generally not as efficient as boilers, and their capacity *is* limited. They may also violate the building code in some towns so it pays to check before you use one in place of a boiler. If you use a water heater I strongly urge you *not* to circulate the domestic hot water through the radiant tubing. There's a danger here because the water can lay stagnant in the tubing during the nonheating seasons. It can become a breeding ground for bacteria, particularly the bacteria that causes Legionnaire's Disease. Now, I realize that Legionnaire's Disease is an airborne disease, but I also realize that most folks continue breathing while standing under the fine mist of water that's in their shower. I don't think the risk is worth the savings. Sure, some installers hook up timers to cycle the circulator every few days to keep the water moving through the radiant heating tubing during the summer months, but I really don't think this is worth it from a liability standpoint. It's your call, but if I were going to use a heater instead of a boiler, I'd assign it to *just* the heating system and not the domestic hot water as well. One exception to this is a hybrid product made by Bradford White. They call it the *CombiCor*™ and it has a plastic coil inside the water heater. The coil is a double-walled heat exchanger, which means that should the coil spring a leak the domestic hot water can't mingle with the heating water. This unit has a fairly high pressure drop on the space-heating side and you'll probably have to hook up two circulators in series (one discharging into the suction side of the other) to make it deliver the goods.

If you were a big fan of the Seventies, you'll be happy to hear that solar is making a comeback - if not yet here in North

America, then certainly in Europe. Solar panels and radiant heating go together like Jimmy Carter and Walter Mondale. They're made for each other because radiant doesn't *need* high-temperature water, and solar panels often don't *deliver* high-temperature water. It's a marriage made in heaven and I suspect we'll be seeing more of these up on the roof before long.

Ground-source heat pumps are also taking the place of boilers in many parts of the country. A lot of people still believe it's impossible to heat a home with 50-degree water from under the ground, but then, they also laughed at the guy who suggested you could cool a shopping mall with a steam boiler. There's heat *everywhere*, and even though science can often be incomprehensible, a ground-source heat pump does a mighty fine job of squeezing heat out of the water that's flowing around below your feet. These systems cost more to install, but they make sense in the long run. I believe they'll play a bigger and bigger part in hydronic radiant heating as time goes by. Watch.

You can mix the ancient with the new if you'd like to take a radiant zone from your old steam boiler. In my book *How Come?* I spent a chapter showing how you can take a hot water zone off the base of a steam boiler. You can do this without a heat exchanger by taking advantage of the natural law that says "If you hold your finger over the top of the drinking straw, you can draw the straw from the Pepsi without spilling it on your lap." Trying to do this with radiant, however, is not a good idea, though, because the water in a steam boiler is *filthy* and the tubing in a radiant system is long and narrow. Long and narrow does *not* get along well with filthy. If you want to use your steam boiler to make your floors warm, use a heat exchanger and two circulators (one for the boiler side and the other for the radiant side). You'll also need a compression tank and all those other neat hydronic accessories on the radiant side.

Beyond the Boiler Room

BOILER
ROOM

C H A P T E R   10

. . . .

Beyond the Boiler Room

You have to get the warm water from the boiler to the man-ifold sets and here you have a couple of choices. You can use either hard or soft pipe. "Hard" pipe is pipe made of metal. Usually it's copper, but it could also be steel, although why you'd want to go to the extra trouble and add all of that ferrous metal to the system is beyond me. You'll follow the same common sense piping practices you've been using for years. The only dif-ference here is that the pipe ends at a manifold set instead of at a radiator or convector.

You can also use "soft" pipe, and here I'm talking about PEX or rubber hose. More and more installers are choosing this option because these materials are so much easier to work with. You can use long lengths of PEX or rubber. It's light. It's flex-ible. You don't have to solder it. You won't risk burning down the building. There are far fewer joints. All in all, soft pipe has a *lot* going for it. In my house here on Long Island we've had a kick-space heater in our little kitchen for the past four years or so. It's piped to our boiler with ³/₄" Heatway rubber hose. That hose has been seeing 180-degree water all this time and it's working just fine. We chose Heatway because we had to snake the connections behind some cabinets and this seemed like a pretty easy way to get the job done. It was!

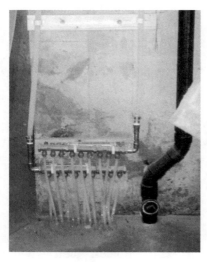

Here's a photo from a job where the contractor used Wirsbo PEX tubing between the boiler and the manifold sets.

This is so much simpler than hard pipe don't you think? PEX expands a lot, though (about twice as much as copper), so you have to be careful in how you guide it through the building. Make sure you anchor it in the middle of its length so it will expand equally in both directions instead of all on one side. That's to prevent any creaking noises that will either scare or annoy the homeowners. Here's a photo of the tubing being guided along the ceiling of a high-end home. Notice the plastic guides holding the PEX tubing to the beams.

If you choose PEX, make sure you leave enough room to make your turns. PEX that measures $1^1/4$" and $1^1/2$" needs a pretty wide turning radius. If you kink PEX tubing,

you can heat it to get rid of the mistake. Remember, because it's a macromolecule, it will always go back to the shape in which it was originally crosslinked. But on a job, you don't want to have to start taking down pipes of this size to heat them, do you? Just make sure you don't make the turn this tight!

Laying out the Tubing Circuits

When you hook up a tubing circuit to a manifold, one end of that circuit is going to get the supply water and the other end is going to bring the return water back to the boiler. That's obvious, but I'd like you to give some thought to *where* you're going to direct the hottest side of that circuit, and where you're going to lay down the colder side. You have a choice, you know, and there *are* two sides. You can just drag that tubing into the  room and start stapling it to the floor anywhere you feel like it. A lot of installers do just that. They look around, shrug, and say, "Hey, whatever fits, babe!"

Smart installers know better. They know that the greatest heat loss in a room is near the outside walls, windows and doors. That's why they'll always run the hottest tubing that way first. By doing this, they'll add extra warmth to a place that's naturally cooler so the people will feel more comfortable. Remember the people will be losing BTUs to that cool surface. By adding heat to that point you'll be helping them counteract that personal heat loss.

Here's another advantage of doing it this way. The air that comes in contact with a cool wall, door or window wants to fall toward the floor. That sets up convection currents in the room, something you're trying to avoid in the interests of greater comfort. By focusing the greatest heat near the coldest surface you'll balance that falling air and put it in check.

I remember visiting a new office building in Germany that was still under construction at the time. The engineer had specified hydronic radiant heat for the tiled floor of the five-story atrium lobby. Since there was a wall of glass that soared five stories in the air, the engineer also specified decorative hydronic convectors that spanned the width of the glass. He placed a row of these radiators at every floor level. He knew that when hot water flowed through these convectors the air that was trying to fall off the cold surface of the glass was going to meet warm air moving upward. The two forces canceled each other. You'll be doing the same on a smaller scale when you run the hotter side of the circuit near the coldest surfaces of the room. Here are a few examples of what I'm talking about.

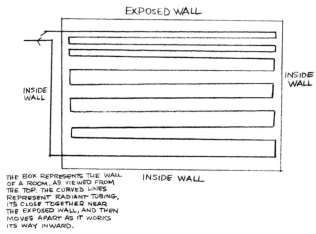

THE BOX REPRESENTS THE WALL OF A ROOM, AS VIEWED FROM THE TOP. THE CURVED LINES REPRESENT RADIANT TUBING. IT'S CLOSE TOGETHER NEAR THE EXPOSED WALL, AND THEN MOVES APART AS IT WORKS ITS WAY INWARD.

This room has one wall exposed to the outside. You'll run the hot side of the circuit that way first to take advantage of the hotter water that's going in that direction.

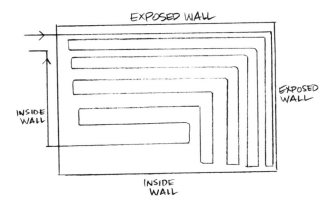

Here you have two exposed walls. See how the tubing has both of them covered? It's common sense, right? You just have to plan ahead.

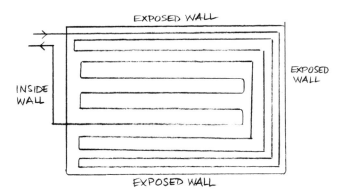

Finally, we have an addition to a house. It has three walls exposed to the cold outdoors, so the hot side of the circuit reaches all the way around before working its way inside. Nothing to it!

If you're working with rooms that are going to have different floor surfaces, say, a rug here and ceramic tile over there, try to give each its own circuit so you can regulate the temperature by adjusting the flow to each. The room with the rug is probably going to need hotter water than the room with the ceramic tile. By slowing the flow to the tiled room (which you'll do at the manifold) you'll be able to keep the water out there longer and cool it down a bit more. The exception to this would be a case where you have a master bedroom with a rug that's adjacent to a master bath that has ceramic tiles. It's okay to put these on one circuit if you have to because if the flow through both rooms is the same, the bath will just naturally feel warmer than the bedroom. Remember Mr. Wizard? Rug feels warm! Tile feels cool! In this case, tile feels warm and rug feels cooler. That's because you're warming both at the same rate and with the tile, there's less insulation between the people and the hot water inside the tubing. Got it? Good!

Try to keep a walk-in closet on its own circuit so you can adjust the flow. If there's too much heat going into a closet the people are liable to pass out before they can get their clothes on. You can adjust the temperature by adjusting the flow, and the more control you give yourself over that flow the easier your job will be.

For the same reason, keep a room that's exposed to a lot of sunlight on its own circuit. If you're putting tubing in the slab of a sunroom, consider using a slab-temperature sensor instead of an air thermostat. More on this later.

All in all, if you just use the same common sense with radiant that you would use when zoning any other system, you'll do just fine. For instance, don't try to heat the basement and the second-floor bedroom on the same circuit. Just use your head, okay?

When you pipe from the boiler room to your manifold sets, you'll usually do it with a two-pipe system. Here's what one of those looks like.

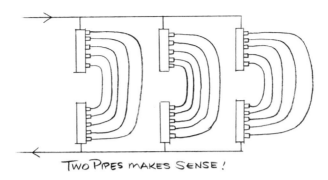

TWO PIPES MAKES SENSE!

This is a two-pipe, direct-return arrangement. As you can see, we're feeding three supply manifolds and returning water to the boiler from three return manifolds. The tubing that you'll install in the floor gets attached to these manifolds.

Now, the big advantage of two-pipe when you're working with radiators or convectors is that it lets you deliver the same temperature water to every unit. Say, for instance, that you had a length of baseboard in this room over here and another length of baseboard 100 feet away. By using two-pipe you could be pretty sure the water temperature entering each of those two convectors would be more or less the same. But compare that to a one-pipe system. Let's say you ran the water through that first convector before you sent it on its way to the second. The second one would get cooler water, wouldn't it? Sure it would! And that's the big disadvantage of a one-pipe system. With one-pipe, *all* the water passes through *all* the convectors on its way around the house. It gets colder and colder as it goes. That's why there's a practical limit to how much baseboard you can put on a one-pipe circuit. If you use too much, the water will get too cool. It might not be able to heat the rooms at the end of the circuit on the coldest day of the year. When you feed heaters with two-pipe, there's really no limit to how far you can go and how many heaters you can use, as long as you insulate that supply pipe.

We don't use one-pipe to feed manifold sets because that would look like this.

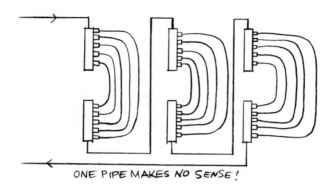

ONE PIPE MAKES NO SENSE!

Imagine how cool the water entering that third supply manifold is going to be. It's already passed through the first two manifold sets, for Pete's sake! Think, too, of how far the water has to flow to get to and from the boiler. Every drop has to flow through every manifold set. And since we figure the size of the circulator on the pressure drop across the longest circuit in the system, you will be looking at one whopper of a circulator. Don't do it.

Manifolds

The manifold we've been talking about is the place where the pipe breaks down into a number of smaller pipes. It's a point of distribution for the radiant panel and I'm sure you've figured that out by now. The pipe between the boiler and the manifold is sort of like an arm that reaches out into the building (the boiler, I suppose, would be the torso). The manifold then becomes the hand at the end of the arm. The little spuds that come off the manifold are like the knuckles of that manifold "hand." (How am I doing?) The circuits (the tubes that you'll attach to the spuds) are like splayed fingers that stretch across the room.

And then it all works its way back to the boiler. Pretty simple, eh? Here's a manifold set.

Manufacturers make mani- fold sets from copper, brass, or plastic. There are several ways to make the plastic tubing or rubber hose connection to the metal or plastic of the mani- fold. You can have a compres- sion type of connection, or a barbed connection, or a clamp, or whatever. It all depends on the manufacturer. Some installers make up their own manifolds and they've come up with some pretty clever ways of attaching the tubing. There's room for creativity here, but just make sure the method you  choose holds the tubing well or you'll be cleaning up a mess.

Generally, it's a bit difficult to get the tubing onto the mani- fold. This is *good*. You see, there's this thing called the "Easy On/Easy Off!" Rule. You don't want the latter, so you try to avoid the former. Wirsbo uses a connection that involves a ring of PEX that fits over the tube, for instance. You use a special tool to expand the PEX, which you then slip onto the manifold spud before the PEX has a chance to shrink back to its original shape. The method takes a bit of practice, but it's not that hard to do. Remember, since PEX is just several macromolecules it will always want to shrink back into the shape it was born in. I visited their factory in Apple Valley, Minnesota once and watched as they put some lengths of PEX through some torturous tests. They had a sealed length of 1" diameter PEX in a tub of 180- degree water. They raised the pressure inside the tube until it exploded. It took about 750 psi to make that happen. The tubing blew out, but the connection held fast. In another test, they stretched a length of tubing on a machine that looked like the hydronic equivalent of a medieval rack. They applied about 375 psi and yanked the stuff out like taffy until it was the diameter of a BIC® pen. The fittings held. They took the PEX off the machine, heated it, and it went right back to its original shape. Pretty spooky.

I am convinced that when manufacturers have produced enough PEX, this stuff will attempt to take over the world just like the Blob from that 1950s movie. But whatever happens, I *will* believe in those connections.

I mentioned this earlier but it pays to say it again. If you have a manifold set with more than five circuits, it's a good idea to arrange the circuits in a reverse-return order, wherein the first tube supplied is the last tube returned. This gives you better flow balance.

For zoning individual circuits, you might consider using a device called a Telestat, which is similar to an electric zone valve, but it goes right on the manifold. The Telestat opens and closes, usually at the call of a space thermostat, to let the water flow where you need it.

Telestats have had their difficulties over the years, and many installers prefer to zone in other ways. They'll use small balancing cocks at the manifolds and arrange the manifold sets so that each serves one zone, and then they'll balance them manually by making small adjustments with the balancing cocks. Some installers will label these for the homeowner so the homeowner can make small changes as needed in the future. Other installers believe it's best for homeowners to keep their hands in their pockets.

Where you put the manifolds is your choice. On most jobs, they wind up outside the boiler room, hidden in closets, under stairs, or in cabinets made especially for this purpose.

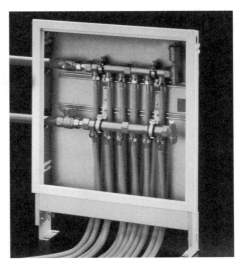

Some contractors prefer to use just one large manifold, which they place in the boiler room. This manifold can have dozens of connections feeding out to circuits throughout the whole house. Sioux Chief makes this sort of manifold, and you can get it with tiny ball valves that allow you to balance and isolate each circuit. Make sure you label everything as you install it. You don't want to have to go back later and try to figure out what goes where after the tubing is buried in concrete.

Insider tubing tips

I've listened to dozens of contractors who have done hundreds of hydronic radiant heat jobs across the country. Here's what they've told me about the right and the wrong ways to install hydronic radiant tubing.

Slab installations Figure out where your manifolds are going to go and then install them before you do anything else. Set them up at least two feet above the floor and hang them temporarily on some scraps of wood or pieces of rebar. Don't do the tubing first. I talked to a guy in Wisconsin who did all the tubing first. He then tried to plug all the ends into the manifolds. The trouble was he forgot which one went where. He was able to blow air through them and match them up, so he didn't think that was such a big deal. He didn't know what went where, but he figured there wasn't much he could do about that at that point (so much for comfort control!). And then he found that some of the tubes didn't reach the manifold. Some were too long. Those he cut, but others were too short. He wound up patching pieces together with a repair kit and he told me the end result looked pretty sloppy. And by the way, the customer made a point of mentioning this to him. Now he does the manifolds first.

If your manifolds are going to be inside an outside wall, make sure both the manifold and the tubing wind up on the warm side of the wall insulation. You don't want these things to freeze. If you think there's a possibility things might freeze, put some antifreeze in the system (more on this later).

If the manifolds are going to be inside a cabinet, make sure you bring your tubing up from under the manifold so the tubes

 don't stick out too far from where the floor and the wall meet. Use protective sleeves over the tubing to protect it from expansion and contraction wear at the point where it emerges from the concrete. Tubing manufacturers sell these sleeves.

When you're laying out your tubing, make sure your first row is at least six inches away from the outside wall. That's to protect it from the carpenters and the rug guy when they start driving their nails. Make sure *all* the trades know where your tubes are.

Use a tubing uncoiler. If you don't have one, you can rent one from your wholesaler. If you're working with PEX and you don't have a tubing uncoiler you will need the dexterity of an orangutan to get the job done.

When you attach the tubing to the floor or the wire mesh, use the staples or ties that the tubing manufacturer recommends. Other fasteners might wear away the tubing at the point of contact. Don't use duct tape. The glue will eat the PEX and you will be one very sorry installer.

Fasten the tubing every three feet, or less, to the wire mesh on straight runs when you're doing a slab installation. Don't over-tighten the ties or the staples. You don't want to stress or crush the tubes. And watch out for any sharp edges on the rebar or wire mesh.

Don't leave PEX out in the sun. The ultraviolet rays can break it down. Keep it covered when it's on the job site.

Don't install radiant tubing right next to a toilet's wax gasket. (The horror! The horror!) There's a company called Predco (1-800-323-6188) that makes a product they call the Ultra Seal. This takes the place of a wax gasket and it's perfect for toilets that find themselves on a radiantly heated floor. They make the Ultra Seal from PVC, which is resistant to heat. It adjusts to different piping materials. It won't restrict the flow. It forms a positive seal and it's easy to install. Check it out.

Label each circuit and write the length on each one. You'll be glad you did once the concrete's down because it will help you balance the flow later on. Don't exceed the loop lengths you laid out in your design. A good rule of thumb is to keep your maximum circuit length under 250 feet. That keeps you in the range of "normal" circulators.

Pressurize each manifold to at least 50 psi overnight before you lay down your concrete. Don't be surprised if you see a pressure drop of up to 10 psi as the tubing expands overnight under the pressure. Just make sure it doesn't drop off any more than that. Keep the pressure on the tubing while you're laying down the concrete. And make sure the tubing doesn't float up when you're doing the pour. If possible, use compressed air instead of water to keep the tubing under pressure. Air is better than water because if the air leaks from the tubing, it won't affect the composition of the concrete. Water will.

Protect the manifolds from concrete splatters. You have better things to do than chip concrete off of threaded fittings, right? The concrete guys are not thinking about you, pal. Neither are the painters. For the same reason that you don't want to put tape on PEX (bad chemical reactions!) you don't want to paint it either. That didn't stop *these* painters, though. Here, check out what they did on this job.

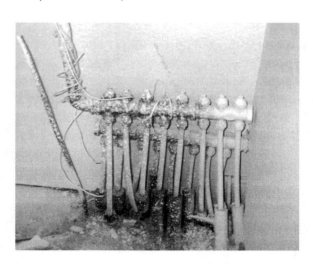

Pretty nasty, eh?

If the tubing is going in a slab, the slab will have control cuts so that the slab will break along definite lines if it has to. Know where the control cuts are going to be and sleeve the tubing if it has to pass beneath one of those control joints. Avoid passing a tube under a control joint if you can.

As a rule of thumb, here's how much tubing you'll need for the job. As you can see, it all depends on how you space it.

Tube spacing	Amount of tubing you'll need (per square foot of floor surface)
6" centers	2.05 linear feet
8" centers	1.65 linear feet
9" centers	1.38 linear feet
12" centers	1.05 linear feet
15"centers	.83 linear feet
18"centers	.7 linear feet

I have an old study that the Bethlehem Steel Company did back in 1949. It shows that the efficiency of hydronic radiant tubing lessens when you space them closer than one-and-one-half times the slab thickness. For instance, if you have a four-inch-thick slab and you place the tubes closer than six inches, you're really not getting your money's worth. Which is probably just as well because it's not practical to put the tubing any closer than six inches – especially if it's PEX. If you bend PEX too much, it will kink, and then you'll have to get out your heat gun.

Staple-up installations This is like lacing a high-top sneaker. You'll be drilling through the floor joists to make the holes. The tubing will be your "laces." Don't drill a hole in the joists larger than 1¼", and always drill the hole in the center of the joist. You don't want to weaken the structure of the house and have it crashing down upon your noggin, do you? It's perfectly okay to run the tubing under the joist bays if the folks are not planning to finish the basement ceiling. Don't do that over a crawl space, though, because the tubing might freeze at the point where it sticks out from the insulation.

Run the hot side of the circuit to the cold walls first. We talked about this before, remember? Alternate hot and cold tubes between the joist bays if you can. Here's a sketch of how you'd do that.

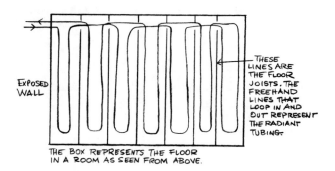

EXPOSED
WALL

THESE LINES ARE THE FLOOR JOISTS. THE FREEHAND LINES THAT LOOP IN AND OUT REPRESENT THE RADIANT TUBING.

THE BOX REPRESENTS THE FLOOR IN A ROOM AS SEEN FROM ABOVE.

Staple the tubing every six inches so it stays in contact with the floor. Don't drive the staples in so far that they distort the shape of the tubes.

Pay especial attention to any old wiring you find in the joist bays. If you raise the ambient temperature in the insulated joist bay above what the old wiring can take there's a good chance you'll be blowing fuses. You might even start a fire. That's not good. Right?

And stay away from the toilet's wax gasket. Arrrggghhh!

Use $^3/_8$" or $^1/_2$" diameter PEX for staple-up rather than the $^3/_4$" size. The smaller stuff is easier to work with. Or better yet, consider using Heatway's more flexible products for this application. Their hose costs more than PEX, but it will save you time on staple-up jobs and time is money, right?

CHAPTER 11

· · · · · · · · · ·

Controlling the Comfort

It was a weekend I will not soon forget. On October 21, 1995 I was walking through a beautiful park in downtown Denver, Colorado. It was 70 degrees F and it was Saturday evening. I had just finished the first of two days of training at the Denver Pipefitters Apprenticeship Training Center. I was looking forward to the next day, and then to my flight home from Denver's brand-new international airport.

I woke on Sunday morning to a bit of a surprise. The temperatures had plunged into the low 20s and the Weather Channel was predicting snow. I finished the class around 4:00 PM and drove to the airport. Snow began to fall when I dropped off my rental car at around 5 PM. By the time I got to my gate, the airport was closed! This was *never* supposed to happen to Denver's new airport. It happened because *I* was there. I finally landed in New York at 5 AM the next morning.

But you know what? As I sat in the airport for hours that night I realized, once again, that there will probably never be a National Standard for controlling hydronic radiant heating systems. There are just too many weird weather conditions to consider. Here on Long Island, it gets cold, but once it does, it stays that way. We don't get the bizarre shifts in the weather that my Colorado friends regularly see. The control strategy you need in Colorado is "reset." On Long Island, you can get by with simpler things.

"Reset" is short for outdoor-reset control. What it means is that the control will "reset" the temperature of the water to compensate for a change in the weather. When it gets colder outside, the control makes the water that's continuously flowing through the system warmer. As the weather warms up, the control does just the opposite. It lowers the temperature of the water that's flowing through the radiant system. Reset is like putting cruise control on your house. No matter what sort of "hills" the weather throws your way, reset maintains the "speed" you've selected for that system. If you say you want to go exactly 70 degrees F at all times, that's as fast as your house will go. It's totally automatic once you set it up.

So when the temperature goes from a gorgeous 70 degrees F on Saturday evening to a miserably windy 20 on Sunday morning, you've got it all covered.

Here on Long Island, I could get pretty good control by just starting and stopping my circulator off a room thermostat. Would I rather have an outdoor reset system? You bet I would! That's the good stuff. In fact, even way back in 1948, the Bethlehem Steel Company thought so too. Here, listen.

The outdoor-type instrument designed to properly modulate the temperature of the continuously circulating water to exactly balance heat losses from the structure at any given moment is the best method of control yet devised.

And it still is – but you don't always need it. Here again, from Bethlehem Steel in 1948:

In spite of theoretical objection, ordinary room thermostats have been used widely and satisfactorily in hydronic radiant heating sys-

tems. That they have been able to maintain satisfactory comfort con-
ditions is largely due to the fact that in small enclosures air temper-
atures tend to more nearly approach average surface temperatures
than is the case in large rooms, so that air temperatures in the small
installation are more nearly an index of comfort.

That's a pretty long sentence, but you get the point, right? A
lot has to do with the size of the place you're heating as well.
This is also why we'll probably never have a National Standard
for controlling hydronic radiant heating systems. We don't all
live in the same size house with the same size rooms.

On Long Island the weather stabilizes at Wet, Frigid and
Miserable during most of the winter. Because it does, we have a
lot of radiant zones running off of simple space thermostats.
Smart installers choose the thermostats offered by the folks who
sell the tubing because the manufacturers calibrate these a bit
differently for radiant heating systems. They do this to take
advantage of the heat storage capabilities of the floor.
Controlling the comfort doesn't have to be complicated at all!

Speaking of thermostats, for years the Hydronics Institute
has suggested that installers use two-stage thermostats on
hydronic systems. The first stage of one of these thermostats
controls the circulator, starting and stopping it according to the
temperature in the room. The second stage operates the burner.
It works like this. Let's say there's a call for heat. The circulator starts and runs, trying to move hot water from the boiler to
the zone that needs it. The burner doesn't fire right away with a
two-stage thermostat because there may already be hot water in
the boiler. If another zone just shut off, for instance, the water
is probably still hot, right? There's really no reason to start the
burner again if there's hot water in the boiler, is there? Of course
not! So the circulator just runs and tries to satisfy the zone
without starting the burner. If it can't, the temperature in the
room will continue to drop, and that's where the second stage
comes in. It will start the burner at a certain point and heat the

water that's already flowing to the zone. A two-stage thermostat saves fuel because it doesn't automatically start the burner on a call for heat.

Earlier, I told you about Alan Levi's family room where I learned more than I wanted to about staple-up systems and hot, humid days. His was a tough room to heat. It had three exposed walls, lots of glass, skylights, a fireplace, and a cathedral ceiling, and it was over a crawl space. We put radiant tubing under the floor, but Alan wasn't sure that would be enough on the coldest day of the year so he left his original baseboard convectors in place. He figured they'd help out when the temperature dropped way down there. He could have used a two-stage thermostat to control this room. The first stage would have operated the radiant zone's circulator (he used a three-way valve to lower the water temperature). The second stage would have operated another circulator or zone valve to send water through the baseboard convectors. This would have come on only when the weather was at its worst. But since Alan already had the original thermostat in place, he just added another. But he *could* have gone with the two-stage had he been in a two-stage mood.

The homes in Levittown that I've told you about had a very simple control strategy. They maintained temperature in the boiler and had just one zone, that being the radiant floor. They put the circulator on the return and pumped toward a tee that had a bypass going right up to the boiler supply. In the run of the tee, just before the nipple went back into the boiler, they placed a $^3/_4$"x $^1/_8$" bushing. Whatever water could fit through that $^1/_8$" hole could go back into the boiler. And naturally an equal amount of water would flow out the supply side of the boiler to mix with the water that was coming up through the bypass loop. Since there was only one zone, the Dead Men were able to get reasonably good control by cycling the circulator on a room thermostat. If they maintained the boiler at 180 degrees F, the water flowing out to the floor would be 140 degrees F. If someone came along and raised the high-limit setting, the cat would wind up on the ceiling. MeOW! But I wouldn't recommend you do your modern systems this way. Why drive a covered wagon when beautiful, late-model cars are available?

If you're putting radiant floor heating in a place that's going to get a lot of sun, consider using a slab temperature sensor instead of an air thermostat. The slab sensor will keep the surface of the floor at a certain temperature all the time. That's a good way to deal with a space such as a sunroom where it may feel fine when the sun's out but too cold when the sun ducks behind a cloud. The slab sensor doesn't care about the air temperature; it's just going to give you that constant source of warmth from the floor.

You should also consider using a setpoint control if you're heating a wood floor. This is a good way to avoid heating the wood too much. If you make the floor hotter than 85 degrees F you might dry the wood too much and that can lead to excessive cracking.

No matter how you decide to control the comfort in the room you'll be working with relatively low-temperature water. You need water that's hotter than this to run your indirect water heater and the zones where you're using baseboard convectors, fan coils or panel radiators. Let's take a look at some easy ways to get several temperatures out of one boiler.

How to lower the water temperature

A radiant zone will almost always run at a lower temperature than a zone with hydronic convectors. If you have a system with more than one thing going on, you'll have to run the boiler at high temperature, and then lower the temperature of the water flowing to the radiant portion. Here are a few ways you can do it off of a primary loop.

Two-way valves: Let's say you size a radiant zone that needs 4 gpm flowing out to the tubing at 120 degrees F. Figure it comes back from the radiant panel at 100 degrees F. That gives you a 20-degree temperature drop across the floor on the coldest day of the year. Chances are good that about $3^{1}/_{4}$ gpm out of that total flow of 4 gpm will recirculate right back to the radiant panel. The other $^{3}/_{4}$ gpm flowing out to the system will be the 180-degree hot water from the primary, boiler loop. This will bring the return water temperature from 100 degrees F up to 120 degrees F. It doesn't take much. It's like when you're in the shower. You only have to add a *little* hot water to make the cold warm, right?

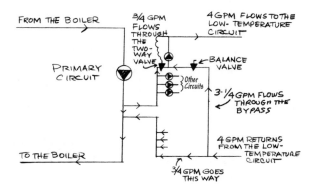

Naturally, $^{3}/_{4}$ gpm of 100-degree return water will leave the radiant circuit and enter the primary boiler flow at the same instant the $^{3}/_{4}$ gpm of hot water goes out to meet the recirculated water. The neat thing about using two-way valves is that they don't have to be large. In this case, you'd probably use a $^{1}/_{2}$" two-way valve, and even *that* size would be larger than you need. Remember, the smaller the valve, the lower the cost.

You can get a two-way valve that's self-contained. It would have a probe that sticks into the radiant panel's supply line. It will maintain the temperature of the water that's flowing out to the floor. You can also get these valves with motors that work with outdoor-reset controls. These can regulate the temperature of the water to suit the needs of the moment. Danfoss makes this type of valve.

Once you realize you don't need that much hot water to raise the temperature of the flow moving out to your radiant panel you might want to try something a bit different. Most installers run large (typically $1^1/2$") pipes between their boilers and their manifolds. They do this because they often feed more than one manifold set with a single branch line. But you can probably deliver all the hot water you'll need to a radiant panel with a $^1/2$" or, at most, a $^3/4$" line if you think it through. Here, check this out.

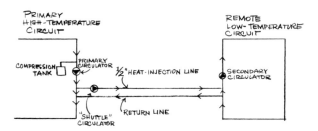

You have your boiler loop, and it has its own circulator to protect the boiler against low-temperature return water. The radiant panel also has its own circulator. Both circulators are relatively small because they're concerned only with the flow of the boiler and the panel, respectively. Connecting the two loops together is a $^1/2$" line that also has its own circulator. It, too, is a small circulator because it's moving such a tiny amount of water over a relatively short distance. You're using the principles of primary/secondary pumping to move hot water from the boiler to the radiant panel. Why would you want to do this? Because it's often easier to snake a $^1/2$" line through a building (and hide it) than it is a $1^1/2$" line. You should have as many options as possible, right?

Three-way valves: You can also lower the temperature of the water by using a three-way valve. Here's how that will look in your primary/secondary system.

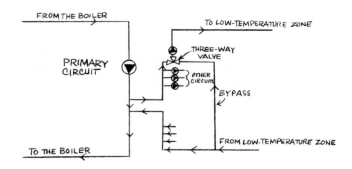

The three-way valve can be self-contained; in which case it will supply just one temperature to the radiant panel. This is fine for simple systems, but if you want to have your radiant panel running on reset, you'll use a three-way valve with a motor. The valve takes water from the boiler into its "hot" port and mixes it with the water returning from the radiant panel, which it receives through its "cold" port. It then sends warm water out through its "mixed" port.

Three-way valves are usually going to have to be the size of the pipe that's supplying water to the radiant panel, so they're going to be larger, and more expensive, than two-way valves. Use three-way valves *only* if you have a primary/secondary piping arrangement. Don't use a three-way valve if the water from the radiant panel is going to flow directly back to the boiler.

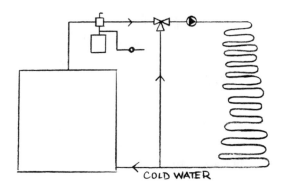

Can you see what's wrong here? The water that's not flowing back to the radiant panel is going directly into the boiler. Without that primary flow to raise its temperature the return water stands a good chance of damaging the boiler. If the flow is large enough, it might cause flue gas condensation or thermal shock to the boiler. Don't use them this way.

Four-way valves: These are relatively expensive but *really* popular because if you pipe them the right way, they'll protect the boiler no matter what happens. A four-way valve has four ports.

Two of the ports are for the boiler and two are for the radiant panel. Follow the flow path through the valve. Notice how the hot water from the boiler does two things. It raises the temperature of the water returning from the radiant panel so warmer water can go back out there and continue to make the people smile. It also

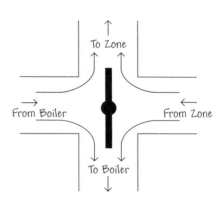

raises the temperature of the water that's returning to the boiler to prevent thermal shock and flue gas condensation. Within a system, the four-way valve looks like this.

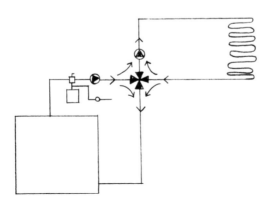

Notice that I'm showing you two circulators here. One is serving the boiler and the other takes care of the radiant panel. It's important to have two circulators when you're using a four-way valve. Some manufacturers publish drawings showing four-way valves with just one circulator. They always place that circulator on the tubing side of the four-way valve. I don't think this is such a good idea and I'll tell you why, but first you have to accept the Rule of the Tee. This is the rule that states, Whatever *enters* a tee must *leave* a tee. Can you buy into that? I sure hope so, because if you can't, none of this is going to make any sense.

Okay, we begin with the acceptance that a four-way valve has two jobs: It regulates the water temperature to the radiant panel, and it protects the boiler from low-temperature return water. Let's take a look at what happens if you use just one circulator.

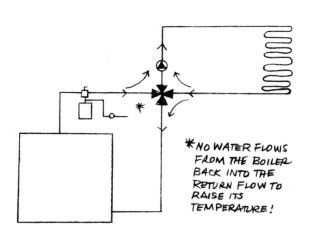

*NO WATER FLOWS FROM THE BOILER BACK INTO THE RETURN FLOW TO RAISE ITS TEMPERATURE!

When a circulator runs, the highest pressure it can produce will be right at its discharge flange. The lowest pressure will be at its suction flange. Since high pressure will always head toward low pressure, the water moves from the circulator's discharge back to its suction. Keep this in mind, and remember that whatever goes into a tee must leave a tee.

Now trace the flow pattern based on the pressures this single circulator will create. The water will leave the discharge of the circulator and flow through the radiant panel, right? When it returns to the four-way valve, it will treat this valve exactly as it treats a tee. Now, please remember that whatever goes into a tee *must* come out of that tee. The same rule applies to a four-way valve. Some of the water will flow through the four-way valve and go right back into the suction side of the circulator. From there it will take another trip through the radiant panel. But not all the water will go that way. Some will flow through the boiler and pick up some heat. The water will come out the other side of the boiler and join up with the water that has bypassed the boiler entirely. You know what's wrong with this? The four-way valve is supposed to protect the boiler against that low-temperature return water. It's not doing that in this case, is it?

Take another look at the drawing and reason this out. Some of the hot water from the boiler is supposed to flow through the four-way valve and join with the stuff that's coming back from the radiant panel. It would certainly do that if you had that second circulator, the one that serves the boiler loop. But without that circulator, water can't flow that way because the pressure on the return side of the boiler is greater than the pressure on the supply. That's because the boiler itself has a pressure drop. Since low pressure can't go to high pressure, no water flows from the boiler side of the four-way valve into the return stream from the radiant panel. The four-way valve acts exactly like a three-way valve. And I already gave you the reasons why you should *never* use a three-way valve on a boiler – flue gas condensation and possible thermal shock.

No matter what you might see in some valve manufacturer's literature I don't think you should *ever* use a four-way valve with just one circulator. I've discussed this with several valve manufacturers and they weren't able to show me how they can make it work. If I were you, I'd play it smart and use that second circulator.

Injection systems: Go back to the section on two-way valves for a moment and find the drawing where I showed you how to use a ½" line to move hot water between the boiler loop and the radiant panel loop. This is the way an injection system works, with a few significant differences.

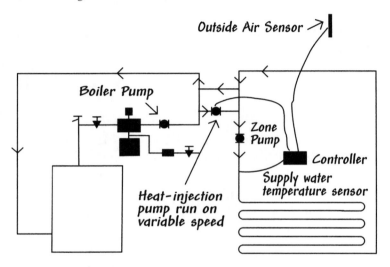

An injection system uses a control that tekmar, the Canadian controls company, manufactures. The control is about the size of a Sony Walkman® and it does a *lot*. First, it senses the outdoor air temperature. Then it operates the system on reset, changing the temperature of the water flowing through the system to meet the needs of the moment. The control operates a standard circulator that acts as a hot water injector between the boiler and the radiant panel. What's significant about this control is that it's able to run the injection circulator on variable speed, speeding it up and slowing it down as needed. This gives much closer control than an injection circulator that just starts and stops. The control also makes sure the water temperature in the boiler is always 15 degrees F hotter than the water in the radiant panel. Pretty smart, eh?

A wholesaler friend in Colorado called me during the spring of 1997 and told me he had just gone through a winter where he was a bit concerned because he had sold a few hundred of these controls during the previous year. "I wasn't sure what was going to happen with them. I hoped for the best, but there was no need for concern. We had only two callbacks, and both involved bad field wiring." Right now, this device from tekmar represents the state of the art in hydronic system control as far as I'm concerned.

Tapping into an existing high-temperature zone for a radiant circuit: Let's say you're remodeling a bathroom and the folks have baseboard convectors. You might suggest they replace the convector with radiant heat, which you can then install under the tile floor or behind the new tile walls. Here's how you do it.

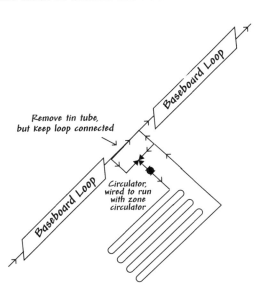

Use what you've learned about primary-/secondary pumping to tap into that existing baseboard loop. Get rid of the fin-tube and connect the loop together with copper tubing. Then, install two tees very close to each other. Take the hot supply off the first tee and run it to the hot port of a self-contained three-way valve. Pipe your circulator off the "mixed" port of the three-way valve. The recirculation line goes into the three-way valve's "cold" port, and the return goes into the other tee you piped into the baseboard loop. You can put the circulator and the three-way valve inside their vanity if you want.

You'll wire the new circulator in series with the circulator (or zone valve) that's already serving the baseboard convector loop. That will make the radiant zone a "slave" to the baseboard zone. The thermostat that controls the baseboard zone will also control the new bathroom. It's another option for you. The more options you have, the better off you'll be.

Radiant circulators?

A big part of control has to do with where you send the water and how much goes which way, and that's where the circulators come in. First, let's clear up some semantics. What's the difference between a circulator and a pump? Well, when you use a centrifugal pump in a closed system you call it a circulator. When you use a centrifugal pump in an open system you call it a pump. That's it. It's just a way to distinguish where the thing's going to wind up. In a closed system the circulator doesn't do any lifting because the water going up balances the water coming down. All the circulator has to do is overcome friction, and if you size it properly it does a beautiful job. A circulator in a closed system is sort of like the motor on a Ferris wheel. No lifting, just turning.

There's nothing unusual about the circulators you'll use in your radiant heating systems. They're the same as the ones you'll use in a system with baseboard convectors or fan coil units. Nothing special, but as you've seen, you can run them continuously with a reset control, or you can start and stop them at the command of a room thermostat. If you use that tekmar injection control you can even run them on variable speed.

There are a few things you need to know when you're selecting circulators for radiant heating systems. Probably the most important is the effect antifreeze has on a circulator's ability to move water. I've covered this in its own chapter (which comes up next), so I'll say no more about it for now.

As a rule of thumb, if you limit yourself to five circuits off of each manifold set, and if you limit each circuit to maximum of 250 feet, you'll stay within the flow rate and head capabilities of the standard water-lubricated circulators that are so common nowadays. If you exceed those limits (and there's no reason why you can't) you'll have to use larger circulators. Or you can do this.

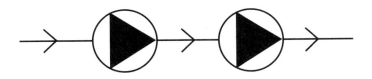

Take two circulators and pipe them this way. The head pressure the two circulators provide will accumulate and you'll have more force to push through long tubing circuits or heat sources with higher-than-normal pressure drops. You can pipe as many circulators as you'd like in series. That's how manufacturers make deep-well pumps. They don't use a lot of pumps, just a lot of pump impellers. They put them all on a single shaft and let the first impeller discharge into the suction side of the next, and so on. The pressure builds and the water comes roaring up from the well. The pumps on fire engines work the same way. I'm not going to go too deeply into this because if you design your radiant systems properly you won't need to use series pumping too often. Just know that it's in your bag of tricks, should you need it.

Stick this in that bag while you're at it.

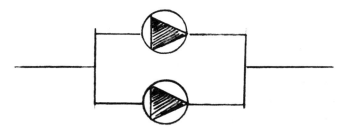

We call this parallel pumping because the circulators sit side by side and share the load. The beauty of this is that if you size your piping and circulators the right way, you can run just one of them most of the time and get not half, but more like 85% of the total flow! It's all in the sizing. Here again, I'm not going to get into too much detail on how to work all this out. If you're interested in learning more about both series and parallel pumping ITT Bell & Gossett has some excellent publications on the subject. And you don't even have to be an engineer to understand them!

One more thing before we move on. I want to give you some flow rate guidelines I've found useful over the years. These are the maximum flow rates you can expect to get through the pipe sizes you'll usually run across when you're doing a radiant system. I'm also showing you the loads you can expect to deliver based on some common temperature drops.

Pipe size in inches	Maximum flow rate in gallons per minute (to avoid velocity noise in the system)	BTUH load at maximum flow rate (based on a 20-degree temperature drop)	BTUH load at maximum flow rate (based on a 15-degree temperature drop)	BTUH load at maximum flow rate (based on a 10-degree temperature drop)
$\frac{1}{4}$	.7	7,000	5,250	3,500
$\frac{1}{2}$	1.3	13,000	9,750	6,500
$\frac{3}{4}$	4	40,000	30,000	20,000
1	8	80,000	60,000	40,000
$1\frac{1}{4}$	14	140,000	105,000	70,000
$1\frac{1}{2}$	22	220,000	165,000	110,000
2	45	450,000	337,500	225,000

What's going to give you different temperature drops? Well, it could come from the design of the system, the length of the tubing circuits, the tubing layout you chose, the temperature of the day, the amount of insulation – things like that. Use these numbers as general guidelines, not as an absolute guarantee of what's going to happen on that next job you do.

Now about that antifreeze . . .

CHAPTER 12

. . . .

Antifreeze - The Chilling Truth

First the good news. Radiant systems that are in slabs are less likely to freeze than other systems because that slab stores a lot of heat. There will be times, however, when you'll want to add antifreeze so there are some things you ought to know about it.

First, know that there's a special type of antifreeze that manufacturers have developed specifically for hydronic systems. Never use automobile antifreeze in a hydronic system. Manufacturers formulate automobile antifreeze to put up with extreme, and frequent, changes in temperature as well as violent agitation. You don't find that going on in a heating system. Manufacturers also expect car owners to change their antifreeze every two to three years. You don't want your customers to have to go through that, do you? Hydronic system antifreeze will last about 12 years, and to make sure that it does, you should check it at least once a year with a hand-held refractometer (an instrument that tells you the percentage of antifreeze in solution).

The two types of antifreeze you'll come across when you're doing hydronic work are ethylene glycol and propylene glycol. Ethylene glycol is less expensive but it's also toxic. Propylene glycol is nontoxic and a much better choice for a radiant system because it won't hurt PEX tubing.

Don't use more antifreeze than you need for protection because it will add to the cost of the job and reduce the system's efficiency (Pay more, get less!). A glycol mix of 20—50% is all you'll ever need, even in severe climates. Here's a chart that will help you figure out how much you'll need. You'll also be able to see the differences in performance between ethylene and propylene here.

Percentage of glycol	Ethylene Freeze Protection	Propylene Freeze Protection
55%	-50 F	-40 F
50%	-37 F	-28 F
40%	-14 F	-13 F
30%	+ 2 F	+ 4 F
20%	+ 15 F	+ 17 F

By "freeze protection," we're talking about a solution that will stay free of ice crystals at a temperature that's five degrees F below the coldest expected ambient temperature in your neighborhood. It makes no sense at all to protect the system to temperatures lower than that. In fact, the more antifreeze you add, the less it protects, and the harder it gets to pump.

Glycol is naturally corrosive to some metals so manufacturers add corrosion inhibitors to protect the metal in the system. The inhibitor will protect steel, cast iron, copper, brass and solder. It will *not* protect galvanized steel, however. In fact, it will attack it. The zinc in the galvanized steel will react with the inhibitor in the glycol and cause solid material to drop out of the antifreeze. That solid material will head right for the tightest turns and spaces it can find in your system and make for some very memorable service calls.

The corrosion inhibitor that they use in hydronic antifreeze also does not get along well with aluminum if the temperature rises over 250 degrees F. Keep this in mind when you choose a boiler. Some boilers are *made* of aluminum.

Before you add any antifreeze, flush the system thoroughly with a mixture of water and trisodium phosphate (TSP). If you can't get trisodium phosphate (it's banned on Long Island because of phosphate's effect on our ground water), use a commercial soap called MEX. You'll find MEX in most paint and hardware stores. You don't need much TSP or MEX. A 1—2% solution will do nicely for the system flush. Let the solution circulate for a few hours and then flush it all out.

Before you fill the system, check the quality of the water. If it's not right it can react with the glycol and create sludge. Be especially careful with well water, and if you're using city water, check the quality of the water the Water Company provides before you use it. Here's what you're looking for:

Characteristics of the water you're considering	Parts Per Million Should be
Calcium	Less than 50
Magnesium	Less than 50
Total Hardness	Less than 100 (5 grains)
Chloride	Less than 25
Sulfate	Less than 25

If you can't get water that meets this specification, use distilled or deionized water.

There's this measurement called pH that you should know about. It's a way of telling whether something is acidic (like sulfuric acid) or alkaline (like lye or Drāno®). The pH scale runs from 1 (*seriously* acidic) to 14 (*unbelievably* alkaline!). Number 7 is right in the middle and we consider that "neutral." Most glycols have a pH that's somewhere between 9 and 10.5. That's relatively alkaline. After you mix the glycol into the water the overall pH will probably drop to a point between 8 and 9. If you're checking the pH and it's reading lower than 8 it's probably because the corrosion inhibitor has lost some of its potency. If the pH should drop below 7 it's time to change the antifreeze.

Do it right away. Drain the system and flush it out really well. That glycol can eat up the metal in no time at all.

Glycol will also affect the circulators you're using because it's thicker (more viscous) than water. It also affects the system's ability to transfer heat. If you're going to be using glycol, make sure the person who's sizing your equipment knows about it. Here, check out glycol's effect on the heat transfer of a 180-degree F glycol/water solution, as compared to straight water at the same temperature.

Amount of glycol	Ethylene	Propylene
20%	4% less heat transfer	3% less heat transfer
50%	13% less heat transfer	10% less heat transfer

When you're using glycol, it's like having a boiler and radiators that are undersized. You have to compensate by using more radiant tubing. And because it is more viscous, you'll have to add 15% to your circulator's flow rate and 40% to its pump head to get the same results you would with straight water. You also have to add 20% to the size of your compression tank's Acceptance Volume. I'm basing these numbers on a 50% mixture of glycol and water, and I hope I'm getting your attention. Glycol makes a *big* difference.

Speaking from the real world.

Mark Eatherton, Colorado Madman, has had more experience than most with glycol. Since I have so much respect for his real world experience with the often bizarre conditions that occur in the Rocky Mountains, I asked him to share with you and me a seasoned installer's perspective on the subject of freeze protection. Here's what he had to say.

"I think you should use glycol only when it's absolutely necessary. Those situations that warrant its use would be on snowmelt (pretty obvious eh?) and in cases where the dwelling may be inaccessible for prolonged periods, or be subject to loss of thermal or electrical power. I would include among these any summer home in the hinterlands that use propane for fuel, and where electric shortages and other unexpected situations occur regularly.

"On snowmelt systems, we'll usually use a 50/50 mix of glycol and water. At this ratio, the fluid has the consistency of diluted maple syrup with a nice purple color. Its capacity to carry heat is less at this ratio than it is with a higher proportion of water. You have to use larger circulators and bigger boilers. If you don't, and if you're using copper fin-tube boilers, the boiler's heat exchanger will howl. Have you ever had a customer call and ask you if you've installed a ghost in their snowmelt system? I have!

"The typical residential system will have a mixture containing 25—30% glycol. Some manufacturers recommend a minimum of 30% glycol to ensure corrosion inhibition, but bear in mind who's selling you the glycol. It's been my experience that in a good clean system, 25% works well. It will protect the heating system to around 15 degrees Fahrenheit for liquidity, and ten below zero for freeze/burst protection. I've checked all the systems that I've induced glycol into after two years and I've seen no appreciable degradation of the glycol's corrosion-inhibitor levels. But then again, we take extra precautions to avoid using too much flux on our soldered joints. We also make great use of big bore PEX tubing for our distribution lines and that eliminates many soldered joints. You see, the acid residue from flux will overcome glycol's corrosion inhibitors quite quickly—typically within a few years or so.

"You should *never* connect an automatic water makeup to a snowmelt system because it's liable to add water to the glycol mix and cause the system to freeze. If the designer or installer is uncomfortable installing a system without the feeder, he should use a low-system-pressure cutout to protect against dry-firing.

"In situations where you have to use glycol, you should use only propylene glycol with a corrosion inhibitor, never ethylene glycol. Ethylene glycol is toxic to humans and animals, and it's made from lightweight petroleum. PEX does *not* get along well with petroleum products. PEX manufacturers say ethylene glycol will make their tubing age at an accelerated pace.

"The Uniform Mechanical and Plumbing Code requires the use of an approved backflow preventer to avoid the possible contamination of potable water resources. Although propylene glycol is a common substitute for sugar in processed foods, its sweetness will still rattle your teeth. I also recommend that you add a red dye to the glycol. That will give the homeowner a warm, fuzzy feeling when she sees a fluid on the floor that is not red. It's probably just Fluffy the dog doing her thing.

"There are two other things that will break down glycol pretty quickly – heat and oxygen. Heat, or what we call pyrolization, occurs at temperatures above 250 degrees F. My previous experience with solar systems that stagnate at 350 degrees F and higher has proven this is true as far as I'm concerned. Oxygen, which you'll get in an open system such as you have with wood-fired boilers and solar systems, will cause the glycol to oxidize. Both of these conditions can create glycolic acid that basically eats copper for lunch. In most hydronic heating systems that are properly controlled, neither of these is of concern. In those situations where the water quality (well water?) is unknown or questionable, I'd recommend that you haul up some city water and use it for your glycol mix. Sulfites, sulfates, nitrites and nitrates can wreak havoc on water quality and pH balance and all of that comes with questionable water. If you're not using glycol and the water is nasty, I recommend you use some other type of corrosion inhibitor. I like "Base Hit" from Hercules Chemical. It's a combination of inhibitors, lubricants and sealants.

"If you're going to use glycol you'll have to install a few extra piping components so you can get the fluid into the system.

Typically, you'll have a drain valve on either side of a ball valve and you'll locate this on the main, preferably just upstream of the system circulator. With the ball valve closed, use a small submersible pump to move the fluid from the five-gallon mix bucket, into the drain valve that's located between the closed ball valve and the system circulator. Pump the fluid through the system until it returns to the mixing bucket. You'll premix the fluids in the bucket, of course. The inside of the bucket should have four marks – one each at three, four, six and 12 inches off the bottom. The marks represent 25%, 30%, 50%, and full. Pretty simple, eh?

"Although I've never seen any manufacturer's recommendations on how often you should check the glycol, I think every homeowner should see a technically qualified, smiling face in his or her boiler room at *least* once a year – and not just to look at the glycol. It takes a spider just a few hours to construct a fine nest in the air inlet of a burner assembly. Once that happens, carbon monoxide production can't be far behind. People *need* us, Dan."

Now you know why I respect the guy so much. He has also helped me to come up with some good answers when I'm confronted with the Hydronic Radiant Myths, which we are about to explore.

MMMMMMMMMMMMMMMMM

CHAPTER 13

. . . .

Hydronic Radiant Myths

Myth #1: It's bad for people with heart conditions

Here's what you'll hear. "Your feet determine your body temperature, just like a thermostat. If the blood leaves your brain and upper torso to go to your feet (to cool them off), you will have less blood flowing to your heart and brain and this will lead to a heart attack or a stroke, which will, of course, kill you where you stand."

And then you'll hear this one.

"People with radiant floor heating begin to have trouble with their legs. They get aches and pains and phlebitis, that inflammation of the veins that got to Richard Nixon shortly after John Dean did."

I usually hear these claims coming from people who are in the business of selling either scorched air systems or radiators. People who sell radiators often consider people who sell radiant heat to be their competitors. One fellow from Europe recently told me that *all* the people in his country who had radiant heat now suffered from leg ailments to such an extent that contractors were no longer putting it in. The government was thinking about getting involved, but had not yet made a decision on this. If I haven't seen anything about this on TV or in the newspapers it's only because the government doesn't want to panic anyone. I should be *very* careful with what I tell people, though. I'm liable to be *responsible* for making millions of people *quite* ill.

This guy sold radiators, of course.

Now why would he lie to me?

Go ask the radiant tubing manufacturers how much tubing they're selling to the folks in Europe. The answer is "Plenty!" Hey, *somebody's* fibbing.

The truth is there is no medical evidence for *any* of these stories, but it sure helps your marketing program if you're selling something other than hydronic radiant heat. Radiant heat isn't going to give you a heart attack, a stroke, or poor circulation in your legs. Don't let them scare you. This stuff has been around for a long, long time.

But then again, I suppose they *could* claim that the mortality rate of people who have hydronic radiant heat is a shocking *one hundred percent*!

They *all* die, don't they?

Some just take longer than others.

Myth #2: Animals don't like it

The aforementioned Mark Eatherton, Colorado Madman, was once left alone with a customer's new home and their two dogs, both of them of the Labrador Retriever persuasion. The woman asked Mark and his fellow workers if they would kindly put the dogs in the garage when they were through working. At that point, the dogs in question were still roaming through the house.

Mark started up the new radiant system and went about the business of checking everything out to make sure all was well. When he was done, he tried to get the dogs to leave the house for the garage. Now at this point in the story, it's important for me to explain that these dogs had a reputation for being *very* user friendly. We're talking Labs here, not Dobermans or pit bulls. Anyway, Mark approached the hounds and made the usual human-to-doggie sounds that will get a positive response from a good dog most of the time. Not *this* time, though. The dogs just snarled at him. He tried again. They bared their fangs. There was no way they were going to leave that warm floor for a cold garage. Try as he might, Mark could not get them to budge. He finally gave up and left them in bliss on their new, warm floor.

Hydronic radiant heat, you see, is something worth growling for. And before we leave this myth, I'd like to share with you a touching story I once wrote. It's about a dog I once knew. His name? Why, it was Meatloaf.

The Sound of Meatloaf

They were waiting for the dog to die. It wasn't that they hated the dog, you understand; they just wanted him to be dead for a while.

He was a used dog. They'd picked him up while on a day trip to a neighboring state a few summers ago. From the dog's perspective, the couple had arrived just in the nick of time. Only two days separated him from the gas chamber, and he sensed this in the way a dog will always sense such things.

He was a cocker spaniel, brown in color, age and history unknown. He looked at the couple from his small cage and whimpered, and this broke the man's heart.

"You want him," his wife said, more a statement than a question.

"Ah, I don't know," the man answered, smiling at the little dog. "He is cute, isn't he?"

"He doesn't bark," she said.

"No, he doesn't," the man admitted. "Might not make the best watchdog."

"Ah, who needs a watchdog," she said. "I can't stand it when they bark."

"He does seem quiet," the man added. "Very well mannered."

"Do you think he's paper trained?" she asked.

"Oh gosh, he *must* be. Look at him! He's no puppy." The old dog sidled up to the front of the cage and pushed his ample body at them. His stubby tail wagged furiously.

"How old do you figure he is?" the woman asked, sticking her finger through the wire mesh and rubbing the dog under his chin. This made the dog moan with delight.

"It's hard to tell," the man said.

"Why do you think he's here?" she asked.

The man shrugged. "I don't know. Maybe he belonged to an old guy who passed away. At least we won't have to paper train him."

The dog stuck his brown snout through the wire mesh, stared with liquid, cocker spaniel eyes, and lapped at the man's fingers. And that, of course, was all it took. The couple smiled at each other, filled out the adoption papers, bought a leash and collar and headed home with the old dog.

"What should we name him?" the man asked as they drove along the Interstate. The dog's head lolled in the woman's lap as she stroked his furry ears.

"How about Meatloaf?" she suggested, looking down at the substantial torso.

The man glanced at the dog and laughed. "That's a good name. Meatloaf it shall be!" He reached over and scratched Meatloaf near his butt, causing the dog to moan quietly.

Meatloaf's first official act upon arriving at his new home was to take a two-pound dump on the beige living room carpet.

"Arggggg," the woman growled as she discovered this new territorial marker.

"Maybe he's just getting adjusted," the man offered as he cleaned up the turd. "All dogs do this when they get to a new home. At least I *think* they do."

"I hope they don't do it more than once," she said. "I don't want to see this again!" she shouted at the dog as he sulked off to a corner of the dining room.

Once he'd settled in, Meatloaf spent most of his time sleeping in front of the refrigerator. He'd lay in the blast of warm air and moan quietly. He'd dream doggie dreams and stink to high heaven. Meatloaf, you see, had this situation with his ears. Cocker spaniels are prone to such troubles.

The couple had spent a small fortune on salves, but nothing seemed to stem the gooey ooze and noxious fumes that flowed and spewed from Meatloaf's hairy ears. No treatment seemed to work.

"He's an old dog," the vet said. "I can operate. Cut some channels down the sides of his ears. That sometimes helps."

"How much?" the man asked.

"Twelve-hundred dollars," the vet answered, "if there are no complications."

"Any guarantees?" the man asked.

"Nope."

And this was the reason why Meatloaf remained in the smelly condition Mother Nature had chosen for him.

Every now and then the woman would kick Meatloaf gently with the toe of her shoe, just to see if he was still alive. He'd slide a few inches across the ceramic tiles, turn his old head a bit to the side, look up at her with his tired eyes, and fart. Then his eyes would roll back in his head and he'd sleep.

Meatloaf snored like an old man with bad adenoids.

"I wish he was dead," the husband said late one night as they lay in the air-conditioned refuge of their bedroom.

"He can't help it if he stinks," his wife said.

"Well then, I wish he was dead for just for a *little* while. Just long enough to give us a break." She poked him in the ribs and he giggled.

Fall came and brought with it a gradual drop in temperature. The husband closed all the windows and turned on the heat one chilly afternoon. Within an hour, their radiant heating system had the floors up to a glorious level of warmth.

And that's when they heard it for the first time. It was a low-pitched moan of pleasure and it came from the kitchen. It was almost human in its intensity, almost arousing in its fervor.

"MMMMMMMMMMMMMMMMM" came the sound. The man and woman looked at each other in bewilderment. "MMM-MMMMMMMMMM!" it came again. They headed warily for the kitchen.

It was the sound of Meatloaf. He had moved away from his spot in front of the refrigerator. He was now lying in the center of the kitchen floor, flat on his furry back. His short legs stretched straight and quivering. His red tongue waggled from his slack jaw like a slice of rare roast beef. His eyes were closed. His doghood stood at attention and pointed toward the ceiling. "MMMMMMMMMMM," the old dog moaned.

"Oh my!" said the woman.

"I think Meatloaf likes our warm floors," the man declared, and with that, the beast let loose a noxious blast of flatulence, driving the young couple back to the relative safety of their bedroom.

Fall gave way to winter's icy grip and the old dog continued his day-in-and-day-out song of pure pleasure, much to the couple's consternation.

"What do you think we should do?" she'd ask.

"I don't know," he'd say, as they eyed the dog warily.

Meatloaf would moan from morning until night, rolling his fat canine carcass like a roast beef on a spit. The only thing that slowed his roll was his ever-present, doggie priapism, which acted like a kickstand every time he tried to turn from his side onto his stomach. "Ruff...ruff...MMMMMMMMM!" Meatloaf would intone as he flipped himself on the warm floor. His stubby back legs would scratch lazily at the tiles.

As winter dragged on, the smell grew increasingly worse. The old dog seemed to be rotting from the inside out as he slowly cooked himself on the kitchen floor. By February, he seemed to be reaching for some great odoriferous crescendo.

"What do you think we should do?" the woman asked.

"I don't know," the man said. "Maybe he'll be done cooking soon. Maybe he'll die."

And then one day, as quickly as it had started, the smell suddenly disappeared. When the couple came down for breakfast, Meatloaf was standing by the sliding glass door, as perky as a puppy. He stared lovingly at a young female poodle in the street. She turned herself provocatively toward him. His doggie eyes glistened longingly as he pawed the warm ceramic tile floor like a young bull. The poodle was more than a bit interested.

"Whose dog is that?" the woman asked.

"Who cares," the man answered as he slid the door open a foot, releasing a bounding Meatloaf on the world.

And the very last sound they ever heard from the warm old dog was a grateful, "MMMMMMMMMM."

Such is the magic, the wonder, and the potential of hydronic radiant heat.

Myth #3: It costs too much

No it doesn't. In fact, it pays for itself in fuel savings. The only choice the homeowner really has is whether he would like to pay for the system as a part of the mortgage, or as a part of the fuel bill. The advantage of paying for it through the mortgage is that a mortgage eventually comes to an end. Fuel bills *never* end. Examine the difference in cost between a hydronic radiant system and a scorched air system because that's what you're really selling – the *difference* in cost, not the whole cost. The *difference* isn't much when you figure it out over the life of the mortgage. Those folks will pay far more for basic cable TV than they will for that radiant system. And when you consider the fuel savings, you realize that if they don't go for the hydronic radiant system, it will be just like signing the contract for a new car, getting the payment book, and then not picking up the car!

The truth is *everyone* buys hydronic radiant heating when they buy a house and turn on the heat.   Some folks just never get to enjoy it.

Myth # 4: If you have radiant, you can't have air-conditioning

Oh yeah? Try telling that to the Germans.
Keep reading, pal.

C H A P T E R   14

. . . .

Hydronic Radiant Cooling

We don't pay quite enough for electricity in America to make hydronic radiant cooling feasible yet, but I'll bet that day is coming. As I write these words, folks in Germany are paying 35 cents for a kilowatt-hour of electricity (on Long Island, we pay 19 cents right now). By the time you read these words we both may be paying even more! That's why radiant cooling is a *very* big deal in Germany. About 40 percent of their new commercial construction gets cooled this way. It's not a novelty anymore. The way they figure it, *anything* that can reduce the size of a fan or a circulator motor is a big deal when you have to pay that much to make the blades and impellers spin around. The Germans install the smallest fans and circulators they can, and then they run them on variable speed to try to save even *more* electricity. Even their escalators won't start until you step on them. And don't get caught leaving the lights on in your room when you go out over there!

In America, we spend a lot of money cooling our buildings. Much of that money goes to run the big fans. In our systems, the fans move cool air through ducts. In Germany, they do things differently. Here, about 37 percent of the electrical power we use for air conditioning goes to run the big fans. The rest goes to the compressor.

Not long ago, the Department of Energy studied some buildings in California and learned that, at peak load, about 20 percent of the air moving through the typical commercial building was outside air. Truth is, we don't need that much fresh air to keep people healthy inside these buildings, but that's the traditional way we do things in America. We oversize. In the average HVAC systems, what's not coming in as fresh air gets recirculated around the building. This often causes drafts (remember how your body loses heat by convection?), and that rapidly moving air also passes around a lot of indoor pollution, which can make you pretty sick.

This is where hydronic radiant cooling makes a difference. It doesn't use *nearly* as much air. In fact, the only air you'll need will be the air necessary for ventilation. That reduces the size of the fan motors to next to nothing! In fact, with radiant cooling, the fans use less than five percent of the energy needed to move all that cold air around a traditional HVAC system. And not only does radiant cooling save your customers money, they also get to be more comfortable. Another plus is that these systems are much easier to zone and control since they run on water, instead of air.

So how do the Germans do it? They make the whole ceiling

cool! And what's great is you can't even tell they're doing this. Look up and all you see is a great-looking ceiling..

It's made of aluminum, by the way. They attach the chilled water tubes to the upper side. Remember earlier when I told you the story about the ice skating rink in Ocean City, Maryland? Remember how that woman at my seminar complained about how cold it was out there by the ice? When I checked the temperature with a thermometer, the air was actually warmer out there by the ice than it was in the seminar room where she was perfectly comfortable. What that ice was doing was pulling the BTUs out of her body. It was affecting her radiant heat loss. The Germans are doing the same thing with their cool ceilings. Sit under a cool ceiling and you feel cool. It's as simple as that. And when you *feel* cool, all the engineers have to do is give you some fresh air that doesn't have a lot of humidity in it. Make sense?

The water they flow through the ceilings isn't as cold as the brine flowing beneath an ice skating rink, of course. In fact, because the ceiling offers so much surface area, the temperature of the water isn't much cooler than the temperature of the air in the room. Since they're not cooling the water that much, they often use ground-source heat pumps and even free cooling from the cooling tower at night. They just pump the water up to that tower, let it flow freely through the cool night air, and send it right back into the building. Free cooling! They do this to save electricity. Oh, those folks are smart! But you'd be smarter *too* if you paid 35 cents per kilowatt hour for electricity. Ridiculous prices are positively inspirational.

In some buildings they'll use concrete ceilings instead of aluminum panels, and cool the ceiling with radiant tubing. Instead of warm water they use cool water and the result is the opposite of radiant ceiling heating. That makes sense, doesn't it? And since concrete holds heat for a long time it also holds "cold," or a lack of heat, for a long time as well. This thermal storage business works both ways, you know. A concrete-based system gives them the opportunity to shift away from the peak hours set by the Electric Company. This saves even more money.

One thing the aluminum ceilings have over concrete, though, is their quick reaction time. Aluminum gives them the ability to quickly adjust the temperature of the ceiling as the comfort needs of the room change. A bunch of people might get together in a conference room and have a heated discussion. It can get pretty warm in there, right? An aluminum ceiling will cool them right down. A concrete ceiling would take longer to respond because of its heavy mass.

While at the big ISH fair in Frankfurt back in the spring of '97 I saw these thin hydronic grids of plastic tubing that you can install behind any sort of wall you can conjure.

Trickle some cool water through those extremely thin tubes and the walls cool down. I had to stare at those things for a good ten minutes before I figured out what they were doing. And then I started to giggle with delight. *Very* cool stuff!

Another plus is that when you stop moving cold air around the building the ducts can be 80 percent smaller than those you

need in a typical, American HVAC system. That gives them more room for living. Not bad!

Seeing for myself

I wanted to meet some engineers when I visited the big ISH fair in Frankfurt in March 1997, so I called my friend Bill Boss at Danfoss, Inc. and asked if he'd help. Bill has more international connections than an AT&T switchboard, and he didn't let me down. He called his intrepid colleague in Denmark, Mr. Fester Garm, who called other Danfoss people in Germany, who called engineers, who all managed to find time to meet with my friends and me.

I was traveling with several contractor buddies from the US and we no sooner got off the plane when the Danfoss contingent, Bill Boss, Fester Garm and Lars Berndt picked us up. They drove us to our first stop, that being the offices of Mr. Peter Scherer, Engineer.

Neither Mr. Scherer nor his associates spoke English and we spoke no German, but Fester Garm and Lars Berndt speak a number of languages so we were in good hands. We sat around a conference table and discussed the European approach to modern hydronics, which, as you know, is different from ours.

The typical year in Germany has a heating season that lasts for 2,500 hours. The cooling season is about 1,400 hours long. Compare that to what's going on in your neighborhood. And while you're at it, remember that they pay 35 cents per kWh for electricity. Mr. Scherer's firm designs radiant cooling systems with aluminum panel ceilings. They run chilled water at about 57 degrees F through these. They know that those cool ceilings will draw heat away from a human body during the summer in the same way that a radiantly heated ceiling (or floor, or wall) will allow regular human beings to hang on to their natural heat during the winter.

Mr. Scherer also realized that indoor comfort during the summer is more about humidity control than it is about blowing cold air on people. He figured that with chilled ceilings above, his people would be able to design their ductwork and fans around ventilation and dehumidification instead of air-conditioning in the traditional sense. That reduces the size of just about everything.

Now as I was telling you, after just a few years in practice, 40 percent of the new commercial buildings in Germany have radiant ceiling panels for cooling. With the "old" method of air-conditioning, the seasonal cost of cooling a building was 25 deutsche marks per square meter (that's about $18.75 US as of this writing). By using the cooling panels, they've reduced this cost to just 10 DM/sq. meter (or $7.50 US). Pretty significant, eh?

Mr. Scherer uses Danfoss variable speed drives to operate all his fans and circulators. These controls sense changes in the system and adjust the speed of the fans and circulators to meet the comfort needs from minute to minute. That saves electricity. His goal is to carefully maintain 55 percent relative humidity in a radiantly cooled building. His systems typically change the air in the building 2½ times per hour. They move the air through big desiccant wheels. Desiccant is a drying agent. You've probably seen this stuff. If you order a package containing something that shouldn't get moist you'll find a small packet marked, "Do Not Eat!" wrapped with the item you ordered. You'll look at the packet, wonder what it is, and then toss it in the garbage. That's desiccant. The same stuff that takes the humidity out of the box can take it out of a building.

Along with the desiccant wheels, they also use these big heat-transfer wheels in some buildings that are the size of Ferris wheels. The air in the building goes out through the top of the wheel, leaving its heat trapped within the wheel. At the same time, the outside air moves into the building, picking up the heat from the turning wheel and sending it right back toward the people.

The aluminum ceilings that Mr. Scherer uses are not just for cooling. He has also designed buildings where the ceiling panels closest to the windows can take 115-degree water during the winter to heat the place. He'll move chilled water through the interior ceiling panels during the summer. His goal for indoor air temperature is about 79 degrees F during the summer and 72 during the winter. That feels pretty good when the humidity's right.

But what about those hot humid days? It does get humid in Europe, you know. We don't have a monopoly on this. So what happens if someone opens a window on a sticky day in July? Won't their ceilings sweat like toilet tanks all over their desks and computers? I asked.

"Nothing to be concerned about!" said Mr. Scherer. He explained that they use an electrical contact in each operable window. If someone opens a window on a day when the weather conditions aren't favorable, the energy management system will raise the temperature of the water flowing through the panel. They use electrical two-way valves to do this. At the same time, they automatically kick in the airside of the system to remove the excess humidity. And how do the ceiling panels know what's going on? Each has an electronic sensor tied into the computer. This also gives them the ability to regulate the temperature in individual rooms. Just your typical German system.

Before I left, I asked Mr. Scherer for his overall impression of hydronic radiant cooling. He smiled, laughed, and answered me in German, which Fester Garm translated.

"It's quiet. It's comfortable. It's *very* economical to run. But it's *expensive* to install!"

But it's what you do when electricity costs that much. Will we be doing hydronic radiant cooling? Probably some day.

Will it be soon? Who knows?

The important thing is it *can* be done.

E P I L O G U E

· · · · · · · · ·

The Great Pickle Puzzle Revisited

So I handed the jar back to the contractor and resigned myself to never being an engineer. I simply didn't know how to make things complicated enough. I'll just have to settle for being a sociologist, I suppose. It never occurred to me way back then that you could possibly coax a big thick pickle into a small-mouthed bottle by firing it from a large enough cannon from a great enough distance. Why, I'll bet that pickle's velocity would most likely encounter enough frictional resistance so as to cause said pickle to morph into an elongated pickle projectile. And then once it cools inside the bottle, it might, like PEX, remember and return to its original shape.

Could pickles, like PEX, be made of a just a few macromolecules?

Has anyone ever *checked*?

Maybe we should form a committee or something. What do you think?

I'll bet Professor Mark Eatherton, Colorado Madman, could put a *potato* into that small-mouthed bottle. Hmmm.

You know what *I* think, pal? I think that *none* of this radiant heating stuff has to be complicated. It's all common sense, and you know *everything* you need to know. And the best part is you now *know* that you know it!

At this point, all you have to do is be ready when someone asks you about it. Speak to them in plain English, using examples regular human beings can understand. People are seeing hydronic radiant heat on TV. They're reading about it in their newspapers and magazines. They're interested. The market's out there just *waiting* for you. All you really have to do is show up with the right attitude and the right answers. When they ask, "Can you do radiant?" all you have to say is, "Yes!" and then get to work.

You don't have to be an engineer to say "Yes!" do you? Nah, you just have to be a Wet Head.

And Wet Heads can do just about *anything*, pal.

Never give up.

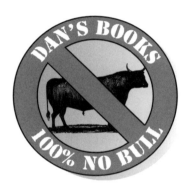

Check out our other books
for regular human beings.
You'll find us on the Internet at
www.danholohan.com.
Or call for our catalog.
1-800-853-8882.